MW00528160

Women Physician Pioneers of the1960s

Their Lives and Profession Over a Half Century

Perspectives in Medical Humanities

UC Medical Humanities Press publishes scholarship produced or reviewed under the auspices of the University of California Medical Humanities Consortium, a multi-campus collaborative of faculty, students, and trainees in the humanities, medicine, and health sciences. Our series invites scholars from the humanities and health care professions to share narratives and analysis on health, healing, and the contexts of our beliefs and practices that impact biomedical inquiry.

General Editor

Brian Dolan, PhD, Professor, Department of Humanities and Social Sciences, University of California, San Francisco (UCSF)

Other Titles in this Series

Heart Murmurs: What Patients Teach Their Doctors
Edited by Sharon Dobie, MD (2014)

Humanitas: Readings in the Development of the Medical Humanities
Edited by Brian Dolan (2015)

Follow the Money: Funding Research in a Large Academic Health Center
Henry R. Bourne and Eric B. Vermillion (2016)

Soul Stories: Voices from the Margins
Josephine Ensign (2018)

Fixing Women: The Birth of Obstetrics and Gynecology in Britain and America
Marcia D. Nichols (2021)

www.UCMedicalHumanitiesPress.com

This series is made possible by the generous support of the Dean of the School of Medicine at UCSF, the UCSF Library, and a Multicampus Research Program Grant from the University of California Office of the President. Grant ID MR-15-328363.

Women Physician Pioneers of the1960s

Their Lives and Profession Over a Half Century

Susan E. Detweiler, MD

with Lillian K. Cartwright, PhD

© 2022 University of California Medical Humanities Press

University of California
Medical Humanities Consortium
Department of Humanities and Social Sciences
UCSF (Box 0850)
490 Illinois Street, Floor 7
San Francisco, CA 94143-0850

Designed by Virtuoso Press

Library of Congress Control Number: 2021952527

ISBN: 978-1-7355423-2-4

Printed in USA

Contents

For Aaron and Amanda
and
In memory of Alec

ACKNOWLEDGMENTS

The thought of writing this book began during a transitional phase for me. I retired from my full-time career as a Pathologist at Virginia Mason Medical Center on the day I turned sixty-five. I had long wished to do a Master of Fine Arts in Writing program, and sixty-five felt like a now-or-never age to do it. I began the Spalding University program a month later.

During the two years of the MFA curriculum, though grateful for the freedom to concentrate on writing, I missed medicine. The idea of circling back to medical school and writing about the study Lillian had shepherded for twenty-five years began to take root. From there, it was an easy step to conceive of a fifty-year completion.

My greatest gratitude in being able to accomplish this project goes to Lillian and to the women physicians who participated. The foundation of the book belongs to Lillian for accomplishing the research and for her insightful analysis of the results. She truly earned her status as the expert on the personalities and careers of women physicians trained in the 1960s in the United States. In doing this fifty-year follow-up, over 80% of the original cohort of women who are alive and able to respond participated in our questionnaire survey or with personal interviews in addition to the survey. I am especially indebted to the eleven surviving women in my UCSF class of 1971 who shared their lives with me on video-recorded interviews.

From my first contact with UCSF School of Medicine administration, Olivia Herbert, Associate Dean and Chief of Staff for Dean Talmadge King, has been unfailingly helpful. Polina Ilieva, UCSF Archivist, offered her expert help in research on the medical school and the female students, including the careful documentation by Robert S. Sherins, MD, of the life and career of Dr. Lucy Wanzer.

My friend and mentor from my MFA program at Spalding University, Dianne Aprile, reviewed almost the entire first draft of the manuscript with helpful critique and advice. Later, Barbara Anderson served as my expert copy editor. In the initial phase of the project, Paul Wink, PhD, Lillian's former colleague, now Professor of Psychology at Wellesley College, participated with valuable assistance.

And with inestimable appreciation, I remain indebted to Brian Dolan, PhD, founder and managing editor of the University of California Medical Humanities Press, whose interest, patience, and encouragement made all the difference in binging this book to completion.

PART I

CHAPTER 1

ON MOUNT PARNASSUS

Mount Parnassus, the Greeks called it mountain of the temple of the god, seemed perfectly named to me as I walked from my apartment on Carmel Street up the hill to the University of California School of Medicine on the top of San Francisco's Mount Parnassus. The school was the equivalent of the house of god as far as I was concerned.

As long as I could remember, the only thing I had ever wanted to be was a doctor. Maybe the seed of desire arose from my second-grade transition from reading every Nancy Drew mystery volume in the San Anselmo Public Library to all of the Cherry Ames nursing books as she progressed from student to army to flight nurse. From these books written during World War II to encourage women to enter nursing as part of the war effort, I recall thinking I would like to be the doctor.

But it was my brother's bloody accident that sealed my decision when I was ten years old. He fell on a muddy metal spike ripping open a large gap in his calf from which gushed a river of blood into our backyard. I ran to get my mother. One glance at her precious little boy, crying and bloody, reduced her to tears. It had been my job to look out for my younger brother from the beginning and, though she never implied that the accident was my failure, somehow I knew I was responsible.

"Mother," I shouted, "we have to get him to a doctor." Though obvious, until I said it, she remained immobilized. I retrieved a towel from our house, wrapped his leg, and somehow got my brother into the car as my mother dried her tears enough to drive to our local doctor. Then the experience turned, at least for me, into something far different from the tragedy reflected in my mother's reaction. I explained to the doctor what had happened, news he calmly received. Easy to fix, he made it clear. He asked me if I would like to watch. I would—and did. He cleaned the wound, by then flushed of mud by the blood which had almost stopped seeping into the discarded towel. He dabbed here and there with various liquids. He sewed the whole bloody mess up. It was the most wonderful thing I had ever witnessed. It was no problem. He fixed it. Then and there, I decided—I would be a doctor.

Despite my decision as a ten-year-old, as I walked up Parnassus Avenue to begin my first day of medical school at age twenty-four, I thought this day would never come. I loved science throughout my education, I took all of the premed courses necessary, I did well academically—yet, despite my qualifications, somewhere in the back of my mind, I didn't think it would happen. "Girls don't become doctors" echoed in my brain. I had never known one. I had never even heard mention of one. No one encouraged me. In fact, it was the opposite. Discouragement came from every corner— my parents, my boyfriends, the few physicians I knew. I stopped mentioning my aspiration just to avoid the negative responses.

Yet there I was, on Mount Parnassus, a member of the entering class of 1967 at the University of California, San Francisco School of Medicine. It would come to pass. All I needed was to study hard and stay alive, and in four years I would be a doctor.

In my class of 135 students, fifteen were female. Having graduated from a women's college, this ratio of male to female seemed quite wonderful to me, but I got over that elation as the class settled in to be "just medical students," all of us packed together on a UCSF conveyor belt designed to make us into physicians. We moved as a single group of 135 from lecture to lecture, lab to lab, usually alphabetized if any subgrouping was necessary—a few females scattered here and there, subsumed into the whole. I remained so happy and grateful finally to be on my way to becoming a doctor, as though reborn to a new life, that being a small minority in the class made no impression on me. It was what I expected. As a national average, 8% of medical students were female in 1967, and, of practicing physicians in the United States, women constituted only 6.7%.[1] At the time, UCSF had no stated policy of encouraging female applicants or increasing the female admission rate. For that matter, the school had no policy for any minority group, yet the overall admission rate of 10% females for the previous four years placed the school above the national average.

If being a small minority in medical school in the mid-1960s did not strike the women at UCSF as odd, it did capture the attention of professionals attuned to psychology and social research at the nearby Berkeley campus of the University of California.

At the time, Dr. Harrison Gough, PhD, was a professor at the Institute of Personality Assessment and Research at Berkeley. Among his several research investigations was the longitudinal study of medical students. He was concerned with how medical students were recruited and selected, a process then based almost exclusively on undergraduate grades and Medical College Achievement Test scores to the neglect of non-quantitative measures such as personality, interests, values, and motivations. As a population for his study, medical students in all incoming classes at UCSF took a comprehensive battery of psychological tests, participated in personal interviews by the staff at the Institute, and were often observed in group interactions. Gough and his associates had thus amassed reams of information on medical students spanning several decades. But it was information with one significant omission. Dr. Gough and his colleagues analyzed these data but confined their investigation only to the male students. The women were given the psychological tests on entry, but their protocols were not analyzed.

At this convenient moment in the 1960s, Lillian Kaufman Cartwright appeared on the scene. She had finished her course work for a PhD, taken

Lillian Cartwright, 1960s, courtesy
of Lillian Cartwright

her written exams, passed orals, and was searching for a dissertation topic. She was invited to come to the Institute and consider working on one of the many existing projects. Gough suggested that she investigate the women who were currently in medical school. Dr. Donald MacKinnon, the Director of the Institute, proposed she look at the architects and other researchers submitted still other groups.

Lillian decided to tackle the study of the women medical students. It seemed to her to be "an arcane subject."[2] That appealed to her. She liked to learn about things few knew or cared about. And that is how I became part of a longitudinal study that would follow us for decades.

Tucked into the orientation material that inundated us in the first few days of medical school, before classes began, was a request to each of the female students from Lillian Cartwright asking if we would participate in her study. We were the final group which would then include every female student, except one, in the entering classes of 1964-1967, a cohort of fifty-eight women.

My participation came with an in-depth personal interview with Lillian which lasted more than two hours. She was, and still is, an engaging woman about ten years older than I, with the insight and ability to view the world in artistic and nuanced ways. In fact, she is a visual artist interested in collages and how images and shapes overlap to build a whole with color and texture. Collages embodied an apt metaphor for how Lillian saw people. She asked many questions centered on my family background, motivation for entering medicine, education, and career aspirations. I liked her and felt rather complimented by her intense interest in me.

Though not anticipated at the time, the study would become the central focus of Lillian's career, and she became a noted authority on the subject of women in medicine.

Based on the psychological tests and interview information on the fifty-eight women comprising the cohort, Lillian obtained her PhD in 1970.[3] In her dissertation, she expanded her findings with comparison to women in other professions and added a historical summary of female physicians in the United States and Europe.

Approximately ten years later, she did it all again, this time aided by a grant from the Robert Wood Johnson Foundation. She contacted the women from the four classes at UCSF and repeated the study: a battery of psychological tests and an extensive, in-person interview. By now we were either finishing our residencies or in early medical practice. She wrote many papers on us that appeared in the psychological and medical literature and was in demand as a speaker at conferences on women in medicine. By then, with growing awareness of the feminist movement, the arcane subject of female doctors had become interesting, in fact, a subject of serious consideration. Then, in 1990, fifteen years after her first follow-up and twenty-five years after the initial study, Lillian did it yet again—another round of psychological tests and a lengthy personal interview. A twenty-five-year analysis of the same cohort of female physicians from a single

Lillian Cartwright, 2015, courtesy of
Lillian Cartwright

medical school followed by the same investigator had never been done. It
was unprecedented. And the timing was perfect. Lillian wrote more papers
on us, she appeared on national news programs on the subject, and she
became the authority on the career arc of women in medicine and their
professional rewards and challenges. Her colleague from Berkeley who
subsequently joined the Department of Psychology at Wellesley College,
Paul Wink, PhD, significantly contributed to the analysis of the cohort in
the 1990 study and greatly aided the fifty-year follow-up that is the basis for
this book.[4]

Over the years, Lillian shared her professional papers with us and
stayed in personal touch with many. I always found it interesting to read
her analysis of our group, whom she came to call *pioneers* as women in
medicine. I even found myself featured as a case study in one article.[5]

Then another twenty-five years passed. After I retired in 2014, the idea
of doing a fifty-year follow-up began to grow on me. A few years earlier I

had taken a two-year leave from my pathology practice to earn a Master of Fine Arts in Writing degree. To write a book based on the extensive information compiled by Lillian and expanded by a half-century follow-up impressed me as an opportunity too good to pass up. Longitudinal studies present enormous challenges, especially ones following a single group over time by the same investigators.

I drove to Mendocino, California, to visit with Lillian at her home perched on a high promontory above the wild Pacific Ocean. She had shifted her career from psychology to art, a major and life-long interest of hers since the age of five when she began scribbling on the walls of her home and making paper dolls. She had studied art at the San Francisco Art Institute among other schools, and had exhibited her work many times in group and solo shows. The lives of people continued to fascinate her. Now, instead of women physicians, she wrote and published about the lives of artists—Georgia O'Keeffe, Alfred Stieglitz, and Donald Judd.

When I told Lillian about my proposal, she was intrigued and said she "thought it was a great idea." She agreed to help. We devised a plan. We would formulate a questionnaire and distribute it to as many of the group in all four classes as we could locate. I would conduct video-recorded, in-depth interviews specifically with the twelve surviving women from my class. Finally we would include archival investigation and consultation at UCSF. Paul Wink, now Chairman of the Department of Psychology at Wellesley College, agreed to help us with his advice and questionnaire formulation and distribution with Institutional Review Board approval from Wellesley College.[6] Lillian and he also tackled the immense job of tracking down the women of the study.

Together, we set to work.

CHAPTER 2

UCSF IN THE 1960s

Although each woman was unique, the women in my class and the three classes before me had much in common. Importantly, our interests and motivations significantly overlapped with those of the men in our classes. Everyone, regardless of gender or ethnicity or race, had a shared purpose. We were in lockstep with one another almost as though we were in the military. The arrangement, particularly noticeable in the first two years when basic science courses dominated the curriculum—anatomy, biochemistry, physiology, microbiology, pharmacology—landed us together, subject after subject, day after day.

Certainly one could sit in a lecture where one pleased, but groupings fell into a pattern too: the eager-beavers in the front row; the cool-guys and cynics in the back; and the majority of us bunched in the middle; the few married couples always together; some budding romances within the class noticeable as new pairings occurred. As friendships developed, little groups gradually defined themselves. But what was obvious, especially in retrospect, was that the women did not sit together as a group. They scattered themselves throughout the room, usually singly. Specific female bonding never coalesced. Over time, some friendships among the women developed, but less frequently than friendships with male students. There were just more men with whom to associate. Though we might joke that we were "one of the boys," it was less about choice and more a testament to the lack of perceived difference. As a class, we were in-it-together in the march toward an MD degree.

Certain subjects required that we divide into subgroups, such as in

Anatomy where four students shared one cadaver. UCSF kept it simple. We were alphabetized. You partnered with the three students closest to you in the first letter of your last name. This approach held true through many subjects and even into clinical rotations. It was almost a military style which eliminated cliques, discrimination, or popularity contests. I don't remember being offended by it. Quite the opposite. After all, medical school in many respects constituted a technical school. The subject was the human body: its plumbing, its electrical circuits, its system of waste and regeneration, its scaffold and muscles. In the matter of grades, UCSF had an equally transparent policy: after a test, a list appeared on the lecture-room door with each person's score, from highest to lowest. You knew exactly where you stood in relation to your peers. This system engendered competitiveness but competition independent of gender.

The faculty at UCSF, with only a few exceptions, was entirely male for both the basic science and clinical years. This was no surprise. It reflected medical education throughout the country. Our male-physician mentors mostly were excellent and, in their dedication to our education, bestowed equal attention to females and males alike. It was admission to medical school that was the gender-specific hurdle. Once accepted, gender was not a significant issue. For example, years after my admission, the committee's evaluation of me was explained to me by Dr. Thomas Hunt with whom I had interviewed. He recalled that some of the committee members voted against me, citing that I didn't "look like a doctor" though conceding that I had excellent qualifications on paper. Fortunately Dr. Hunt defended me. No doubt other women faced hurdles or rejection for similar baseless reasons.

Historically, UCSF had a good record in regard to admitting women. The school began in 1864 as the Toland Medical College, founded by Dr. Hugh Toland who, though lured to California by the gold rush, discovered medical practice to be more lucrative than mining in booming San

Francisco. It was the first medical school west of the Rocky Mountains[1] and the second west of the Mississippi River.[2] Less than a decade later, Dr. Toland transferred his medical college to the newly founded University of California at Berkeley. Within a year, the new UC medical school further distinguished itself when the regents of the university adopted the resolution that "young women offering themselves for admission and passing the required examination must be received to the privileges of the Medical Department."[3] Soon thereafter, Lucy Wanzer gained admission and in 1876 became the first female graduate of the school. Nine decades later, we followed in her footsteps.

If, on the whole, the female medical students were treated like their male classmates by the faculty and the male students, well, we were like the men.[4] In regard to intellect, interest in science, and achievement orientation, the women shared much more with their male colleagues than with any comparable group of women. The psychological tests and interview data collected by Lillian on entering female students bore this out when compared with the Institute's information on male medical students and with studies on other groups of professional women. The only exception concerned motivation for entering medicine. Male motivation was much more apt to center on economic reasons and the prestige of the profession, whereas women more often cited an altruistic desire to help people and/or encouragement by a family member or mentor as motivating factors.[5]

Though the women in the four classes had much in common in respect to intellect, interest in science, and determination, we varied widely in family backgrounds and childhood experiences.[6] I became good friends with three or four female classmates, yet we rarely talked about our past experiences. Our studies and the massive amount of information we needed to learn was more than enough to fill conversations—that and the turmoil associated with the war in Vietnam and the heady, counterculture atmosphere of San Francisco in the late 1960s. My boring childhood growing up in San

Francisco and Marin County had ceased to be of any interest to me. It was the future that was consuming—and that included working for an end to the war.

I never had a conversation with over two-thirds of the women in my class during our four years together. However, in the process of conducting the fifty-year follow-up interviews, I came to realize that our mutual experience, like war buddies who had shared a foxhole, left us with a powerful basis for friendship and open communication about our lives.

PART II

As Lillian and I discussed an organizational framework for this fifty-year report on the physicians in this study, we settled on a format defined by five broad categories based on how the women practiced medicine and developed their careers. Two or three women who illustrated a particular category would be described in detail followed by a more general discussion of how that category fit into the overall follow-up. For example, several women chose a strictly academic career and became professors with an emphasis on teaching or research. They are the "Academicians." A few women had careers that ended far from the starting point, career metamorphosis in a sense. Many women had linear careers similar to mine. I trained as a pathologist and then spent over thirty years being a pathologist. Some women delayed their careers, often to raise young children, and advanced to full-time practice later.

Yet another category emerged that seemed correlated with the background of some of the women. These were women whose parents, and the families of their parents, had faced significant adversity, mostly due to historical events over which they had no control. This legacy united them as "children of adversity" in a way that was not apparent at the beginning of the study, but now, in the final follow-up, seemed salient.

The majority of the women that Lillian and I selected to illustrate the various categories were women from my class who entered UCSF with me in 1967 and who agreed to meet with me for an in-depth personal and video-recorded interview. The interviews enhanced their previous conversations with Lillian and made their lives more vivid to me. I probably would say the same of every member of the original study had I interviewed all of them.

CHAPTER 3

THE SHADOW OF FAMILY HISTORIES

Childhood is carried throughout life as burden or gift or some combination of the two. It shapes the adult. Some of the women in this study had family backgrounds rooted in mankind's darkest history. Inevitably they bore a portion of the burden of their ancestors' experiences.

The Shadow From Europe

The last time I saw my friend Marie Feltin was in 1985.

She swept into the lobby of the Copley Plaza Hotel like a mistral from her native France, parked her bicycle at the nearest potted palm, and waved with a bemused smile as she spied me exiting the grand ballroom amid a crowd of men heading to the restaurant. Marie was surprisingly on time considering that she had pedaled from East Boston to the heart of the *chic* downtown to meet me for lunch. Two doctors could not have looked more different. Marie's long brown hair was a mass of untamed curls. She wore a bright red jacket and a long, Indian-print skirt out of the type of fabric that served as bedspreads in college. Only the absence of a headband separated her costume from what passed as normal in the 1960s. That, and the lack of a black armband with the peace sign—like the one an attending physician at UCSF advised me to remove from my arm when I was a fourth-year student on the private service at Moffitt Hospital. He informed me that political statements had no place in a ward of ill patients. He was right.

Marie and I had dressed more alike back then, both of us in tune with the hippie atmosphere of San Francisco. I was proud to see Marie so unchanged. For myself, I now blended all-too-well with the Brooks Brother style of the Copley Plaza Hotel guests, straight down to my name tag identifying me as an attendee at a Harvard continuing medical education conference on inflammatory and malignant diseases of the skin. There we were, Marie and I, happy to see one another but images of physicians from different galaxies.

During our lunch, Marie told me about her medical practice caring for mostly elderly patients in East Boston, a forgotten bulge of neighborhoods cut off from the city's prosperous core by Logan Airport. She was designing a program to deliver health care that allowed disabled and low-income, elderly patients to stay in their homes. She often visited them herself rather than expecting them to come to her. She described how long it took to help a frail and fragile woman undress, how if you pressed too firmly in taking a pulse you could leave a bruise, and the way a patient's deep breaths during a chest examination might leave him exhausted. I could barely understand how Marie could serve this population, but, beyond question, I could tell she loved it. Marie always had an earthiness about her, and the care she was giving was as bedrock as you could get in medicine. My pleasure in the subclassifications of rare, pigmented lesions of the skin suddenly seemed less compelling.

Of the fourteen women in our UCSF graduating class of 1971, only Marie and I ventured to Boston for our residency training—Marie in internal medicine at the Beth Israel Hospital and I in pathology at the Massachusetts General Hospital. We had little free time in those years. Oddly enough, it was for activities of our domestic lives that we carved out a few hours here and there to get together, often at garden nurseries to shop for flowering plants for our tiny urban plots.

My favorite memory of Marie from those years was when I had my first child in the middle of a snowy Boston night in December of 1973. Like the entire country, the city was in the midst of the gasoline shortage from the fallout of the oil embargo consequent to the Arab-Israeli Yom Kippur War. I had been unsure if my VW Beetle even had enough gas to make it to the hospital in Brookline. Early the next morning, Marie braved the elements to visit me at the old Boston Lying-In Hospital. Like Madeline[1] in an old bed that had a crank, I lay barely awake from the anesthesia of my crash cesarean section of the night before. She cranked the bed down, helped me up, and pushed my IV pole as we walked to the viewing window that displayed the newborns in two straight lines like little muffs of humanity. "He's beautiful," she pronounced of my eight-hour-old son who was anything but beautiful, his head flattened from too long in a breech position below my diaphragm and his skin a moderate shade of yellow from jaundice. To me he was beautiful—and only a generous friend would see that.

Marie's generosity toward people was at the core of her personality. She displayed it from her earliest days in medical school. She instinctively knew how to empathize with patients and simultaneously think through their illnesses. I analyzed the medical problem first and only secondarily acknowledged the humanity that surrounded a diagnosis—as though it were window dressing. This mindset caused one of our classmates to comment, "Detweiler, you're just on a head trip here."

Back in medical school, both the faculty and our classmates recognized Marie's compassionate nature. Each year the UCSF faculty selects three students from the graduating class who exemplify the qualities of a "true physician" for the Gold-Headed Cane Society's annual award. In our year, Marie was among the three selected and, for the first time in the history of the Society, the other two candidates were also females even though women comprised only 10% of our class. It was an "all-female slate" not to be equaled again for almost two decades.

When Marie and I had lunch together at the Copley Plaza Hotel in 1985, I had no idea that it would be our last meeting. Tragedy struck Marie early. She died in 1994 at age fifty. Though her direct voice by interview cannot be part of this half-century follow-up, I met with her widowed husband, Robert (Bob) Master, MD, and brother, George Feltin, MD, who graciously shared with me their memories of Marie. Bob and George each loved and admired Marie, and each knew her well but in different ways. What I write incorporates their stories, mixed with the knowledge and admiration Lillian and I share for Marie. Without including Marie, this story of UCSF female physicians would be incomplete.

Marie's parents, Jeanette and François, were born during the years of the Great War, Jeannette in Poland and Francois in Hungary. Those years were not a good time to be born Jewish in Eastern Europe. They both came from prosperous families that valued education but, when they tried to enter university, were barred in their home countries. So, they did what many young Eastern European Jews did. In 1935, they left for France, then a beacon for Jews wishing to escape anti-Semitic laws.[2] Jeannette and François met and fell in love at the University of Strasbourg in the northeastern region of Alsace, a province on the west bank of the Rhine River that separated France from Germany. Jeannette studied to become a dentist and Francois a chemical engineer.

As Marie's brother, George, shared his parents' history with me, it seemed that they were alert from the beginning to the danger lurking over them from Nazi Germany. In the context of the times, they managed for years to stay one step ahead.

After the Munich Agreement in late September of 1938, Strasbourg became a center of antisemitic propaganda that was smuggled in by Nazi Party members producing riots and attacks on Jewish shops. Jeannette and François left for Paris that year narrowly ahead of the progressive domination of Alsace by the Germans. In fact, by September of 1939 after the German invasion of Poland, the French government evacuated the people living in areas very close to Germany, such as Alsace-Lorraine, including14,000 Jews.[1] Though in Paris, the newly married couple, now officially Jeanette and François Feldheim, had little time to relax.

Through misplaced confidence, almost magical thinking, the French government remained calm in the early months of the war, reality hitting only after the German blitzkrieg tore through Belgium, Luxembourg, and the Netherlands in May of 1940 and bombs were exploding on the outskirts of Paris. Neither French troops nor taxis rushed to the rescue as they had in 1914. Neither the city nor the central government had made plans for the evacuation of Paris. The Wehrmacht invaded France on May 10th; the French Army collapsed within a month. The French government fled Paris on June 10th. In the Compiègne Forest outside of Paris, in the same rail carriage where Germany had signed an armistice with the Allies in 1918, France signed an armistice with Germany on June 22nd.

Paris was on its own. So were the Feldheims.

Parisians poured south in panic, out of the city in trains, automobiles, trucks, buses, anything with wheels. They mixed with the fleeing military to jam the roads. They bolted on bicycles, on foot, in wheelchairs. The Feldheims joined the mass exodus on their bicycles. They slept in fields and forests as they fled south. Somehow, they found enough food and strength to peddle 500 miles into Vichy France and ultimately to the relative safety of an isolated farm near the small village of Calvisson in the southeast, twelve miles from Nîmes near the Mediterranean. With fake Algerian identity cards, Jeannette, François, and a few others managed to live by subsistence farming for the next three years. Food was scarce. At times knives were drawn with their friends over a scrap of bread.

Whatever meager safety Jeannette and François enjoyed in Vichy France ended after Allied forces landed in French North Africa in November 1942. Hitler broke the Franco-German armistice, and German troops formally occupied southern France. The hunt for Jews and partisans intensified. François told his children stories of how he managed to escape by hiding in fields as German soldiers searched the farm and house. Although some local people helped them at great personal risk, the Feldheims' luck expired in November of 1943 when they were betrayed to the Gestapo. With only minutes to spare, four-month pregnant Jeannette and François escaped into the surrounding forest. Starving and desperate, hunted like animals by the Nazis, they managed to survive through the winter. For Jeanette, salvation came at a convent near Nîmes. At the end of January, the nuns gave shelter to nearly seven-month pregnant Jeannette while François continued to hide outside. On April 2nd, Marie was born. Though sick with stomach problems and probable rickets, she lived. The nuns christened her Marie Christine.

Jeannette and François could not have guessed that the war was nearing the end for them after Marie's birth. In June, with Operation Overload bogged down in Normandy, the bloody fighting in the north of France was just beginning. In the south, the grueling Allied slog up Italy had barely reached Rome. Into this desperate summer of 1944, one Allied campaign proceeded brilliantly—the invasion of southern France. Led by the US Army, Allied troops landed in the region of Saint-Tropez on August 15th in order to capture the nearby ports of Marseille and Toulon. Named Operation Dragoon, the campaign routed the Germans on the coast and sent them in a headlong retreat up the Rhône River. Within two weeks, the Allied forces controlled Marseille, Toulon, and the surrounding countryside.

For the Feldheim family, the war was over. Against overwhelming odds, they had survived. From the stories George told me, I imagine that within the struggle to save the life of their infant daughter, Jeannette and François found the courage to face their own future. George said that from the moment of her birth, Marie became François's heart.

As Marie's mother was to learn, she and her sister, Annette, were the only survivors from her family; another sister died fighting with the partisans in Poland. The family of Marie's father was more fortunate within the context of the horror of the time. His parents and four sisters, captured when Hitler invaded Hungary in 1944, were transported to Auschwitz. There, his parents died in the gas chambers, but three of his sisters, assigned to work details in the camp, managed to survive.

After their liberation in southern France, Jeannette, François, and baby Marie remained near Nîmes in the war-torn, impoverished countryside and persevered with farming. Marie's brother, George, was born there in 1946. After a few years, the family moved to Paris and, in 1950, discovered that Jeannette's sister, Annette, had gained asylum in Montreal. Canada's immigration policy allowed the Feldheims to join Annette. After fifteen years on the run from anti-Semitism, Hitler, war, and displacement, Marie's family finally found safety. They began a new life as Canadians.

But a new life was not so easy.

One part seemed an open adjustment to North America. They reconstituted as an extended family with Annette and lived nearby. Eventually, in 1964, François's three surviving sisters managed to join them in Montreal or New York. Though neither of Marie's parents were able to pursue the professions for which they trained in Strasbourg, François found work in construction, and Jeannette worked initially as a dental assistant and later as a clerk in department stores. Life had stability.

Yet much of their life remained cloaked in shadow, never free of their hunted past. After four years in Canada, the family became Feltin, no longer Feldheim, better to have a name that did not advertise their origin. As school forms in Montreal required that the parents state their religion, Marie and George became doubly disguised as registered Protestants for school, hiding even their Catholic baptism in France. They celebrated Christmas. Jeannette and François did not discuss their Jewish identity beyond the confines of the family. Yet when Marie was nine and George was seven, their parents enrolled them in Temple Emmanuel in Montreal. Despite their past, their Jewish ethnicity remained important to the parents. Marie eventually had a Bat Mitzvah; George waited another six decades before he chose to do a Bar Mitzvah. It was confusing to Marie and George—to be living two identities, "hiding in blood" as George said years later in our interview.

This sense of camouflage, of a buried past that could be neither shared nor mentioned, either through shame or fear, stayed with Marie and George throughout their lives. The persecution of the parents became the living history of the children. In her interview with Lillian in 1975, Marie described her father as the German shepherd of the family and the one who shouldered the responsibility. She quoted him as saying, "each move was hard—another life change. You have to start from the beginning each time. I have no real ties to any one country."

George was unabashedly in awe of Marie. In recounting stories from their childhood, George told me that he tagged along behind his bold sister as a willing puppy, happy to be in her presence yet feeling a little envious of the adoration their father showered upon his audacious daughter. Marie had minor conflicts with her mother as a young girl, but once a teenager, mother and daughter became almost inseparably close. The family was loving and harmonious, but George never felt the intensity of union with either parent that Marie did.

What George loved most about Marie was her spunky, strong personality that appeared fearless to him. She would do anything on a dare or for a lark. During the summer after Marie graduated from high school in 1962, she and George travelled to Europe, visited François's home in Hungary, and hitch-hiked around Europe together. It was an exciting time for George to be alone with his intrepid sister. After that summer, George said that Marie became his best friend. It was a bond that lasted a lifetime. Later, after college, George followed his father's advice, went to medical school, and eventually chose to practice as an internist in Boston.

When Marie went to McGill University for college, she lived at home. This was usual for many families in Canada. Her father wanted Marie to pursue a dental career, but Marie decided on medicine by her junior year.

She loved the arts—she played the flute and piano and liked to draw—but didn't think she had enough talent for them as a profession. She enjoyed research and tried it out at McGill with undergraduate projects at the Montreal Neurological Institute and in the Department of Psychology but decided that investigative work did not satisfy her fully. She needed people and wanted to interact with them.

Medicine was the answer.

At twenty-three in medical school at UCSF, Marie was amazed at how popular she became. She was the one true flower-child in our class, fully part of the hippie, counterculture scene of the late '60s in San Francisco and Berkeley. She had not dated much before, and appearances had never been of importance to her, but at UCSF Marie developed into the person she would remain—a free spirit in long, flowery dresses and wild curly hair, unconventional and bohemian. She told Lillian in 1967 that she saw her women classmates as "pretty independent girls who are probably just interested in doing something well. They have needs beyond marriage and children"—but none had the earth-mother as deeply rooted as did Marie. Marie described herself to Lillian as seeking a wide range of experiences, of exploring the world beyond practicing medicine in order to understand herself and where she fit. Her aspiration was to find a place where there was joy, wisdom, and love, and she knew it would need to be a place where she could interact with people. In Lillian's notes, she wrote, "Marie looks unconventional to me at the onset of this interview but, as we talked, I was aware of how attractive she is—not exactly pretty—but massively appealing. She seems to have lived; she has done things; she is spontaneous and a little crazy in the best sense of the word."

This was definitely the Marie that I knew as we shared our lunch at the Copley Plaza Hotel in 1985. She was well on her way to fulfilling her aspirations.

Marie's professional career found its home early in caring for people in the shadows of society—the frail and elderly and those beset with disabilities. I can only speculate that Marie understood their hardships from her own life and family history. She did not view them as helpless and damaged. Instead, she saw people struggling to be independent and to make their lives as whole as possible. She approached them with empathy and respect, perhaps as victims of the winds of life over which they had little control but could triumph with help. Her husband, Bob, said that she had a passion for things that were "less than perfect." She furnished her home that way. I remember from when I lived in Boston, in some neighborhoods, unwanted furnishings were often dumped on the sidewalk. One day, Marie found a discarded rug of oriental design with a burned and ragged corner. She brought it home, cut off the damaged part, covered that corner with furniture, and loved the rug for its inherent beauty.

In the same way, Marie cared for the "not perfect" of society. They were her people. She felt it was the role of medicine, of society in general, to develop accommodation for those with physical or intellectual disabilities *on their terms*, not society's terms, so they could stay out of institutions and maintain control over their lives. Where others might see the damaged and disabled, Marie saw humanity in a struggle to triumph.

After graduation from UCSF and a medical internship at San Francisco General Hospital, Marie continued her training in internal medicine at the Beth Israel Hospital in Boston. She additionally worked part-time at the East Boston Neighborhood Health Center in the adult medicine ambulatory clinics that served a large number of elderly persons. When she completed her residency in 1974, she became Medical Director of the East Boston Home Care Program, a health plan that maintained over a hundred frail elderly in their homes in this gritty, forgotten region of East Boston.

Lillian interviewed Marie in 1975 during her early years with the Home Care Program. Her professional commitment was substantial, constituting sixty to seventy hours per week involved with seeing patients and doing research and paperwork. Yet she felt little role strain despite the heavy workload. She loved being rooted in the community. For Marie, becoming the medical director of a program that maintained a vulnerable, elderly population in their homes was the turning point in her professional life. She had found her identity. "You can make yourself whatever you want—nothing is imposed on me," she told Lillian. Marie visited her patients in their homes. Their faces would light up when she entered. They hugged her and she liked that. They called her Marie, not Dr. Feltin. Traditional boundaries between physician and patient dissolved as did the hierarchy of authority among physician and nurses and other support staff.

Marie earned a master's degree in epidemiology at the Harvard School of Public Health in 1976 and developed the expertise to track the financial outcome of the emerging care delivery systems that she implemented over the next twenty years. Along the way, she obtained more than five grants to design and enact home care systems. She became a recognized expert in the field. Additionally she authored nine professional papers and abstracts on the evaluation of care for the elderly and disabled in independent living situations. Though Marie may have been more relaxed in her ability to hug her patients and meet them on their own turf, she was all-business in her analysis of their health care. She proved that her approach was cost-effective delivery of excellent medical care.

In 1977, while remaining the medical director of the East Boston Home Care Program, Marie and several other physicians, including her future husband, Bob Master, MD, discovered that they were all caring for a similar population of patients—elderly, usually uninsured people, often with disabilities—who would get lost in the system. It was difficult, nearly impossible, to track information on patients as they bounced among hospital admissions, discharges, stays in nursing homes or intermediate care facilities, visits to emergency departments, and their home care by physicians and nurses. Follow-up became disjointed. To solve the problem,

Marie and the others decided to band together—five physicians and seven nurse practitioners. They cofounded the Urban Medical Group in Jamaica Plain as a nonprofit group practice.

It was a free-wheeling time. They did whatever was necessary to deliver care with a *just do it and worry about finances later* attitude. The Urban Medical Gorillas became their facetious in-house moniker. Bob Master credits Marie with the vision and values that defined the group. He paid attention to the finances and structural organization. The Beth Israel Hospital cosigned a loan to give Urban Medical working capital to renovate an office and get started. Marie and one of her colleagues started the disability program with a grant from the Robert Wood Johnson Foundation and an enhanced fee-for-service reimbursement pilot model from Medicaid. With her focus solely on her delivery of care to her disabled patients, Marie drove around East Boston in her old Fiat, patient-encounter forms stuffed in the trunk, with magical thinking about the finances, according to Bob. He fished the forms from her trunk, submitted them for reimbursement, and kept the adventure afloat. Urban Medical survived financially but just barely; $32,000 per year for each physician was the most they could pay themselves. Yet, when we talked, Bob recounted those years as creative, productive, and medically very satisfying. As a group, they wrote a paper, published in the prestigious *New England Journal of Medicine* in 1980, appropriately entitled "A Continuum of Care for the Inner City: Assessment of its benefits for Boston's elderly and high-risk populations."

The bold adventuresome child remained alive in the adult physician. Marie kept her long hair and flowing skirts, ten fingers not enough for her many rings, two wrists encircled by bracelets with charms and bells. In thinking back over our times together, I never saw Marie dressed other than as a free spirit. Long after her death, Bob told me something I never would have guessed. Her long skirts were also for concealment. Marie's legs were deformed with severe bowing, probably from rickets in utero and early infancy.

Marie and Bob became a couple in 1981. Along with his love and devotion to Marie, Bob brought his own complicated past to their relationship. The Vietnam War had exacted its toll on his life, as it had on many of us, and precipitated decisions he might not have otherwise made. On the eve of his deployment to Vietnam as a battalion surgeon in 1969, he impulsively married the wrong woman, not a bad woman, just the wrong one. I understood all too well; I had married the wrong man as he, too, left for the war. Now, five decades later, the feelings of anguish and fatality with which we faced that war are as vivid today as they were then. By 1981, Bob was divorced and the primary parent for his three children between ages six and ten. Marie became their stepmother.

To her overwhelming joy, Marie had a son, Jonas, in 1983 and a daughter, Sarina, three years later. Both Bob and George affirm that not only did Marie desire to become a mother for herself, but she also felt it was something important for her parents, almost a duty, conceivably to erase the deaths of so many family members in the Holocaust and to prove that the family would continue to survive. Marie finally identified openly as a Jewish woman with the birth of Jonas who perhaps served, according to Bob, as her tribal entry into Judaism.

My hope as I write about Marie now, fifty years after we first met, is that the next ten years were the happiest of her life. She had long wanted a child but had trouble finding the right partner. Two long-term relationships had floundered in part because the men rejected the prospect of fatherhood although otherwise the friendships had been deeply meaningful—and fun for Marie who could indulge her adventurous side with conga dancing, drumming, and carefree amusements. With motherhood, she settled down to a more traditional role. She had always been comfortable in the nurturing, maternal, care-taking part of a woman's life. With the birth of her two children, she reduced her work to part-time. She found pleasure in cooking

Marie Feltin and daughter,
courtesy of George Feltin

Marie Feltin and son,
courtesy of George Feltin

and feeding her family and guests. Her parents came from Montreal, often to the point of virtually living with Marie and her active household of five children. Some aspects must have been stressful. Integrating three teenage stepchildren with her younger two presented challenges although Bob took primary responsibility for his older children. In Lillian's interview with Marie in 1990, however, she said, "we truly have a blended family—all the kids are great and they are healthy" and, one of the most satisfying aspects of motherhood, "is the joy of playing with the children; I love to see them growing up."

And Marie, like a few of her medical school female classmates, chose the right man to marry. She and Bob shared the work of both their home and professional lives. She referred to her relationship with her husband as a "twin-ship" and gave it a rating of "5" on a 5-point scale. Fortunately their areas of interest and expertise overlapped well; they could take call for each other. Most importantly, though, they shared values, tastes, and philosophies of life. About Bob, Marie told Lillian, "we are the best of friends."

Though Marie reduced her patient care hours with the birth of her children, her workload remained significant. Beginning with Jonas's birth in 1983, she sequestered enough time in the next several years to write a book, *A Woman's Guide to Good Health After 50*, published in 1987 by the American Association of Retired Persons. The 367-page book covers every aspect of women's health from skin, face, and hair to sexuality to drug dependence to end-of-life issues. Each chapter is interlaced with wit and humor as the book marches through every organ in the body, explained in straightforward language and filled with commonsense advice for physicians and patients alike. It begins with "Older women have never been so young" and ends with "Death is the inevitable end of life, and we will summon the courage to meet it when the hour comes." Prophetic words.

Over their ten years of practice at The Urban Medical Group, the group became less of a good fit for both Marie and Bob. Bob left in 1985 to work with the Massachusetts Medicaid program during the second term of the administration of Governor Dukakis. Marie departed in 1988 along with a nurse-practitioner partner and one administrative person to start the Boston Community Medical Group (BCMG). This was the third health care group to be founded by her in fourteen years. The organization maintained an exclusive focus on direct care for individuals with complicated disabilities and was financed by a unique Medicaid fee-for-service model. This model subsequently led Bob and a finance partner to start the Community Medical Alliance, the nation's first prepaid care system contracting with Medicaid to provide the totality of care for BCMG disabled persons and Medicaid-eligible AIDS patients financed by risk-adjusted global payments.

The achievement of Marie's vision, idealistic and humane in the extreme, demanded an enormous amount of work. When Lillian met with her in 1990 when she was forty-six, Marie was working between fifty-five to sixty hours a week at BCMG with about 60% of her time in direct patient care and 40% in supervision and consulting. She carried her beeper full-time, and it interrupted all aspects of her life. She took only one week of vacation per year. Her salary was equally meager at $51,000 per year. "My practice now harasses my life—my patients are so fragile—80% are between thirty-five and sixty-five years old; and 20% are geriatrics. I see lots of spinal cord injuries, polio, and multiple sclerosis. About 95% are on federal or state-funded care. At least 60% are wheelchair bound. Treating disabilities is not that sexy," she told Lillian. Yet despite the difficulties she experienced at work, Marie said that she was "extremely satisfied with her work." She was abundantly aware of the financial sacrifice she made by her choice of medical practice. But with her practice decision, she also reported that her self-concept changed because of her work. "It makes me more satisfied that I am contributing to justify my existence. I am very privileged to have an insight into the problems and joys of others. I have an inside window into life. In working with the disabled, I have great respect for those who have

overcome amazing obstacles as well as for those who don't quite make it."
As she said, "It is a conscious decision that I have chosen to work with the
underdog—and it is a creative partnership. I have really experienced self-
fulfillment in medicine."

Marie's achievements extracted a personal price. For my generation
of professional women, the price remained unacknowledged even by our
closest supporters. It was the hidden tiger in the shadows. Marie could
see the stripes but others did not. Her husband said that she worked part-
time after the birth of her children. Since when is working fifty-five to sixty
hours per week part-time? Her brother reported that Marie mainly "just
took care of the children after their births"; he failed to see any portion of
her work week. The enduring female dilemma: if you complain about the
added work entailed with raising children, the message twists in the wind
into one that casts a negative shadow on you and your children. Marie
couldn't do that. She loved her role as mother too much even to hint at the
price it exacted. And her personality prevented her from the only solution
that some women managed—hiring others to share the work, to clean the
house, cook the meals, and watch over the children for intervals. The tone
of her last conversation with Lillian in 1990 verged on burnout. When asked
what would constitute an ideal practice, she answered, "I would become a
dermatologist. When I advise other young women what to do in medicine,
I say—think twice before you do what I do." But then she went on to say,
"If somebody had really talked to me (*before starting*), I probably would not
have listened—no one was a great role model. Faith Fitzgerald (a UCSF
physician) was great but (*her model*) only great when you are single. There are
high sacrifices when you are married and have children."

Marie did it all. She couldn't help herself from doing it all.

In the spring of 1993, after returning from a trip to Arizona, Marie
developed a sudden left-side homonymous hemianopsia—the bilateral loss
of the left half of her visual field. Nothing innocent would cause this. Her

medical evaluation brought a death sentence: glioblastoma multiforme, a malignant brain tumor, the most-deadly human tumor known to medicine. It lurked in her right occipital lobe.

People often talk about a *battle with cancer*. Obituaries repeat such statements. There is no battle with glioblastoma. It is a massacre, the tumor always the victor. I know the horror of that diagnosis for Marie and Bob. My beloved husband, Alec, was also its victim. In a nanosecond of viewing his brain MRI scan, we knew that the life we loved together had received a death sentence. Marie's brother George recounted a moment soon after her diagnosis when he and her parents were with her. Marie let out a shattering "animal scream" of primordial rage against her destiny. George said that at the moment of Marie's scream, his father's heart tore in two. François never recovered.

Marie did what she could in face of the inevitable. She had two surgeries, radiation, and chemotherapy. Nothing altered her fate. At some point, she began to accept her certain death and, while she could remain functional, she turned her concern to her children and parents. As the glioblastoma continued to grow, it pillaged her spirit and personality. Marie died on October 28, 1994. The tumor robbed her father of his spirit too. He followed his beloved daughter to the grave four years later. Marie's strong and resilient mother lived with George and, until her death at age 104, continued to help her grandchildren. The family that Jeannette and François preserved through ravages of war and displacement remained together to the end.

Marie's legacy as a doctor and advocate for disabled and chronically ill patients is honored in many ways. Through the Boston Center for Independent Living, a nonprofit advocacy organization for people with disabilities, her husband and children established an annual Marie Feltin Award which is given to persons or organizations that exemplify the spirit and vision that Marie brought to medicine. Marie's Place, named in her honor, is a mental health crisis stabilization home jointly administered by the Commonwealth Care Alliance and the Massachusetts Department of Mental Health. Many of Marie's classmates from the Class of 1971 continue to contribute in her honor each year to the UCSF School of Medicine.

Strength From Christianity

Of the women in our class at UCSF, the story of the life of Dr. Helene Olson (Johnson) surprised me the most. As with many of the women, I didn't know Helene during the four years we shared as classmates nor had I heard news of her since graduation. When she accepted my request for an interview for the follow-up project that Lillian and I were conducting, I was grateful for her participation. From the tone of our email exchanges in arranging our meeting, I could sense reluctance.

For the interview in late September of 2017, I drove the 100 miles from Chicago to Helene's home in Berrien Springs, Michigan, and felt proud of myself for managing the almost two-hour drive and arriving on time at our agreed hour of seven a.m. Until our interview concluded, I remained unaware that I had been an hour late. That Illinois and Michigan occupied different time zones never occurred to me. But by the time I understood my mistake, Helene and I had established rapport and, with a bemused smile, she forgave my cluelessness.

The drive gave me a preview of the southwestern part of Michigan where, with an exception of only six months, Helene had lived since she finished her internship in June of 1972. The small village of Berrien Springs, populated by fewer than 2,000 inhabitants in the 2010 census, is in Berrien County. Bordered on the west by Lake Michigan, the county is noted for its rich agricultural land and apple orchards.

Helene's home sits on the edge of a small lake separated from her son's home by a well-kept lawn that leads to the shore and a dock. The main floor of her home faces the morning sun through huge, light-filled windows. Obviously the center of activity, it is a large comfortable space for kitchen, dining area, and living room. I was immediately impressed with the numerous toys for children along one side. After our interview, I realized that this home was the antithesis of any that Helene knew from her childhood.

Of the fifty-eight physicians in our original cohort, approximately 8% had childhoods that only can be described as unhappy with emotional or economic deprivation—or both. Helene's childhood fell into that regrettable group.

Her parents were German Jewish refugees in London where they met and married during WWII. They had correctly read the currents of the chaos and antisemitism in Europe and the Third Reich in the 1930s and fled. Her parents almost never spoke of their experiences during those years leaving Helene with only scant fragments. She knew of one paternal aunt who survived a concentration camp. Helene was born in 1945 at the Charing Cross Hospital, which she pointed out was also Milton's birthplace. Helene, her parents, and her older sister emigrated to the US in 1950, sailing on the *Queen Mary*. Like so many refugees, including Marie's parents, they changed their name on arrival, from Orsokowski to Olson. With some irony, Helene mentioned in our interview that they were the only Olsons in their Jewish Temple.

The hardships of the war and their refugee status exacted a toll on the parents. Her father retained much bitterness toward Germany and overt hatred of Germans. Helene described him as staunch and without emotions, and her mother as "not touchy-feely" and harboring a negative and critical attitude. Though they initially lived in Chicago for six months, the family moved to Seattle where her brother, Steven, was born in 1955. As she, with some reluctance, discussed her family with me, Steven emerged as the one family member for whom she had, and still has, unequivocal love.

The following year when Helene was eleven, the family moved again, this time to San Francisco. In all, they moved homes twenty-seven times before Helene left for college at eighteen.

It was a lonely childhood in which Helene never made any long-term friends. Yet despite her bleak life, Helene made firm decisions. Forbidden to watch Richard Boone in *Medic* by her father, she sneaked her way to viewing it and decided by age ten to become a doctor "to make the world a happy place." Ten can be a pivotal age. I, too, settled on medicine as my career at that age. Other than her love of her brother, Helene recounted no memories of childhood. No photos, no stories—as though her non-touchy-feely mother who was raised in boarding schools replicated the void of her own past in her children.

Helene described herself as "goal oriented" but that is an understatement. From age eighteen, she was on her own financially and emotionally. She said, "I left home at eighteen" with a tone of finality that included "never to return." She felt that was expected. She paid her own way through University of California at Berkeley working, among other jobs, in the food service at International House, a far from pleasant job. There she felt looked down upon and treated like the hired help by well-financed, predominately wealthy, upper-class foreign students. One plus of the job was free food, leftovers scraped, she said, from the bottom of pots from the cafeteria service.

In Lillian's interview with Helene in 1967, she noted how hard Helene had worked throughout college and how academically successful she was. "She drove herself without mercy," Lillian wrote, and she had a major strength in her very high intelligence. She graduated Phi Beta Kappa, fifth in her class of 5,000, with a combined major in physiology and organic chemistry. Those subjects fit her goal of medicine though her favorites were Greek and Roman art, architecture, and archaeology. Her MCAT scores were among the highest in our class.

At UCSF, Helene continued to carry a heavy, extra-curricular work-load, primarily in food service, to finance medical school. Various jobs included "flipping hamburgers," she said, setting pins in a bowling alley, doing physicals at the Modesto prison (officially the Public Safety Center, a jail for male and female inmates in Modesto), and working in the women's section of the Santa Rita Jail in Alameda County during the summer. When Helene graduated, she had only a $4,000 debt that she quickly paid off from her internship salary.

When we talked, Helene had little to say about medical school except that she was very "goal oriented" at UCSF. When pressed, she said she hated neurosurgery and its requirement to learn all the brain neuropathways and liked endocrinology. It was during medical school, though, that she began to think of doing missionary work in Africa.

At this point in her life with neither financial nor emotional support, Helene had accomplished much to be proud of, yet this is not how she felt. Except for one female classmate, she was isolated and friendless within medical school, and for years she had been disengaged from her family. "Maybe my parents were proud, but I was never aware of it," she said. But then, unexpectedly, at graduation with the hooding ritual in which the Doctor of Medicine degree is formally bestowed on each graduate, Helene experienced one of the peak moments in her life. "I signed up to walk in the ceremony and be "hooded." My dad, a staunch, unexpressive German, asked if he could do the honors," she told me. "That day I thought nothing about my own accomplishment but rather that he loved me. I look back on that and do my best to express my gratitude, love, and feelings to those I love along the way and try to overcome the way I was raised. I never knew he loved me until then."

In July of 1971, Helene began her internship at Letterman Hospital, a US Army hospital in the San Francisco Presidio, established in 1898 to provide medical care for the 8th Army Corps poised to embark for the

Spanish-American War in the Philippines.[3] The hospital was named for Major Jonathan Letterman, MD, the chief medical officer for the Army of the Potomac during the Civil War and considered to be the father of modern battlefield medicine.[4] Letterman Hospital was, in fact, the US Army's first permanent general hospital.[5] At the time of Helene's internship, in addition to Vietnam War casualties, the hospital and its clinics offered health care to all active and retired military personnel and their dependents in the Bay Area. Of her rotations, she liked surgery the best but was not accepted into the surgery residency. Instead, they "took guys that said they would stay in the military," she told me.

Then life for Helene changed, seemingly by accident, almost as though an unseen insistent force had come to bear on her future. In order to pursue her ambition to do medical missionary work, she needed to earn air fare to Africa. By a fluke, she answered an ad in a throw-away journal for a temporary position with a medical group in the small rural Michigan town of Berrien Springs. The Southwestern Medical Clinic (SWMC) was a group of five surgeons who staffed the Berrien County General Hospital and additionally did medical missionary work, rotating their time abroad with work in Berrien Springs. The group, founded by Dr. Weldon Cooke in the 1960s, had a strong, Christian evangelical base and focused on providing medical care for the local migrant and indigent populations. Helene's plan was to work for three months, then travel abroad.

Throughout our interview in 2017, Helene was parsimonious with details of her professional life. Much of this attitude arose from modesty. She disliked talking about herself and hated the thought of bragging— even if what seemed to be bragging to her was simply stating facts. Only in recounting her career tally of deliveries did she display enthusiasm for her accomplishments.

She did share with me a book on the history of Southwestern Medical Clinic, *Mission. Medical. Witness. The Stories of Southwestern Medical Clinic,* written by Lila Chandler.[6] Helene's career at the Clinic forms a chapter.

In the book, Chandler writes that after Helene's inquiry about the job toward the end of her Letterman internship, and before she was hired, Dr. Weldon Cooke happened to be in San Francisco for another reason. He took the opportunity to meet Helene. According to Chandler's narrative, Dr. Cook, his wife, and Helene "rode the trolley and ate supper at the wharf. When the bill came, Dr. Cooke tried to pay for their dinner with an out-of-state check, which the restaurant refused. He never carried much cash. So, the broke little intern had to pay the bill."[7] Nonetheless, Helene accepted his offer of a job. "It was something to do," she told me. She packed her belongings in one suitcase and moved to Berrien Springs in the summer of 1972.

Helene, a female, a Jew, and a physician with only a rotating internship under her belt stood out as the antithesis of the other physicians in the group, all of whom were white male Christian evangelical surgeons. After three months at SWMC, she continued with her plan and left, traveling first to Switzerland. Then fate intervened. She decided to return at the onset of winter. Despite reservations from some of the surgeons, she was formally asked to join the clinic. Certainly Helene must have had her own reservations but join she did. She returned to Berrien Springs with the same single suitcase of belongings that she had toted there six months previously.

For the next twenty-five years, the practice turned out to be ideal for Helene's can-do approach to medicine and her willingness to accept any challenge, indeed any request, which arose. Initially the clinic had no internists, so the bulk of her work was internal medicine. She started an intensive care unit. She tackled problems as they came up with any means available—she inserted chest tubes for pneumothoraxes, placed her first cardiac pacemaker using the package instructions, and performed dental extractions when local dentists refused Medicaid patients. After internists joined SWMC, she did pediatrics until pediatricians joined the clinic.

In those early years in Berrien Springs, her professional mode was not unlike a medical missionary in a third world country. At one point she visited Honduras in a missionary capacity but didn't like it. She did not feel useful "passing out pills," as she described her job there. In Berrien Springs she felt abundantly useful and thereafter thought of SWMC as her domestic mission.

But it was when she started practicing obstetrics that Helene found her true calling and avenue for leadership. As the county hospital, Berrien General was where women without medical insurance or on Medicaid delivered their babies. Prior to Helene's participation, the hospital had no organized obstetrical service although Helene had previously started a prenatal clinic in her capacity directing pediatrics. Now she felt empowered to expand the service to obstetrics. Helene recounted that she "saw the need...no one else wanted to do it" and so she "taught herself." Chandler expands on Helene's accomplishments in OB in the 1970s-1980s: "During her training, she'd seen an epidural, so she began offering them" for deliveries.[8] She introduced the Lamaze technique in childbirth; she allowed fathers and family members into the OR during deliveries "because she didn't know fathers weren't supposed to be in the room." She encouraged fathers to participate in the delivery of their newborns.

Helene delivered 15,000 babies over her forty-two-year career in obstetrics, an impressive average of over 350 per year. She particularly liked high-risk obstetrics. Chandler states that the migrant, indigent, Medicaid population flocked to Helene and Berrien General as the place for safe and family-friendly obstetrical care. Some migrant women even planned their pregnancies so that their delivery would occur while in Berrien County. Helene formally established programs through the Health Department for prenatal care specifically for unmarried black teenagers and migrant fruit pickers. Helene said that she especially liked taking care of underserved women.

Helene found more than a professional home at SWMC. She ultimately found an emotional and spiritual home. At some point after joining the group, Helene learned that although the clinic founder, Dr. Cooke, supported her joining the clinic and hired her, the other four surgeons opposed allowing a Jew to join a Christian group. If Helene initially felt ostracized, she did not mention it to me in our interview. Instead she viewed her fellow physicians as "genuine Christian people." In particular, she admired Dr. Schindler, a surgeon with SWMC, whom she said "exemplified the life he professed." She eventually became very close with her other colleagues. Chandler enlarges on the early years of Helene's practice at SWMC stating that the "mission doctors and their wives all had a burning desire to introduce this Jewess to the Messiah" and engaged in a concerted effort that was somewhat tolerated by Helene, but unsuccessful initially.[9]

In our conversation, Helene did not discuss the actual event that precipitated her conversion to Christianity. Rather, Chandler wrote:

> The nurse (a nurse who worked with Helene) became pregnant with her first child, and Dr. Johnson (Helene) took care of her. According to Dr. Johnson, a lot of things happened during labor and delivery. She did everything technically correct, but the baby came out severely brain damaged. She felt it had been preventable and couldn't fathom how it had happened. The situation weighed very heavily on her.
>
> Within a few months, the burden was too much to bear. Dr. Johnson considered that someone larger than the doctors has to be in charge of life, death, and everything in between. Someone else has to be in control because she wasn't. She no longer wanted to believe that humans alone were responsible for everything. She pulled out a Bible and opened to The Gospel of John. Alone with The Word, she read and became convinced that Jesus was, indeed, the Messiah.[10]

In a written, brief autobiography in 2019, Helene wrote of her experience in 1978 in more detail:

> She was a nurse and friend. They were pregnant with their first child. Long labor went through the night. I was in charge. Monitor strip was abnormal and got worse. I was sleeping. Nurse came to me and showed me the strip. I got up and went to assess situation. She was ready to deliver. I put on forceps and pulled baby out. He was severely brain damaged and eventually died at one year of age. This was a turning point in my life and changed pride to humility. I knew then I could not do my job by myself. It was too much responsibility. I decided God gave me any talents and shortcomings I had, and He would be my strength and knowledge. I grew up Jewish, and it was then that I accepted Christ as my savior, companion, strength and could share the weight of my decisions with Him. Growing up Jewish is a guilt-dominated way of living. In my humanity I was heavily burdened with guilt. While now I still try to please people and have them like or love me, I am free of guilt.[11]

In 1979, six years after formally joining the group, Helene became a Christian and described herself now as a "completed Jew" with the conviction that Jesus is the Messiah for whom Jews are waiting. For her, the wait was over. Her life changed to what God intended for her. The absolutes of evangelical Christianity in terms of right and wrong, good and evil, appealed to her. Boundaries became clear, and they provided a sanctuary for her from the godless, if outright evil, external world. In her 1990 interview with Lillian, Helene said, "The church gives me a reason for being. God loves me. There is a plan for me. I am special, and I feel loved by God. Christ is the Messiah, and although I have been in court many times and I am being sued (she was facing a medical malpractice lawsuit), I know that God is aware of what is going on, and I give it over to Him and let Him take care of it. I will give everything for my kids and for my patients. I will sacrifice my body. I do nothing for myself. I doubt if I will ever change. God has allowed this group to exist. They can threaten us and beat us, but we will endure."

In 1999, SWMC transferred Helene's practice to a healthcare center for women in the nearby town of Niles, where she continued her obstetrical practice in a new and improved facility. Berrien General Hospital was converted to a skilled nursing facility/nursing home. This change marked the beginning of the regional consolidation of healthcare in Berrien, Niles, and other nearby towns into what ultimately became the Lakeland Regional Health System. As invariably happens with consolidations into more complex and integrated systems, the previously independent parts had to adapt to a new administration. In 1999, the Niles facility formally became part of the Lakeland Hospital system.

After working for twenty-five years in a practice that ideally suited Helene, the clinic as such was closed. This was a bitter disappointment. In Helene's assessment, she had designed and built an OB practice that respected patients and provided great care with a support staff she had personally trained. In the new Lakeland system, she believed that physicians were neither respected nor supported by the administration.

As an example, she recounted an instance in which the nurses converted the only handicap bathroom to an employees only bathroom. Helene vehemently opposed this. She physically tore the signage from the door. The dispute devolved into almost open warfare.

Helene especially disliked the team approach to patient care in which everyone on a team had an equal voice. She told me that her career was "all downhill" for the next fifteen years as she was "trying to pursue perfection and do the right thing, butting my head against those who had control."

Whereas Helene sounded unyielding in discussing her professional career in our interview, she was more reflective in her written autobiographical sketch. She wrote, "After retirement, I began a new venture doing admission

Helene Olson Johnson, 2020, courtesy of Helene Olson

physicals at a nursing home (to help out). The staff treated me well, respected me, and I soon realized I could have had a more pleasant end of career and imparted more of my experience and knowledge if I had been less intolerant and negative. I should have adapted more to the team approach even if it wasn't perfect. The new environment renewed in me the feeling that I was basically a good person."[12]

At the end of the interview as I was putting my camcorder and papers away, Helene seemed more talkative, maybe because the recorder was off. In the end, she wanted to tell me: "I am a giver, I don't want anything in return. The giver gets more than the person receiving. I don't even want a thank you—but I want love. I want to be loved. I let my children and grandchildren know they are loved."

And Helene is loved.

Among her good decisions, Helene married a very compatible and supportive man. I met her husband, Mark Johnson, and two of their grandsons at the end of our interview. Mark, a quiet Christian man, had been a laboratory technician on the night shift at Berrien Springs Hospital. He was the youngest of twelve children from a family of modest means in Niles. Beginning in her first years in 1972 and 1973 at SWMC, Helene and he would often talk as she covered the night shift. They became good friends.

Then things moved quickly in 1975—an engagement on a Friday and marriage at the local courthouse the next Monday. Their first child, Eric, born in 1976, was followed by a second son, Corey, in 1978. Helene continued her busy obstetrical career which involved many deliveries at night and on weekends. She and Mark initially shared childcare without any additional help, but by 1980, they decided that Mark should quit work and take primary responsibility for the children. In her brief autobiography, Helene wrote that one of her most important decisions was "to have my husband stop working and be available for the kids. I still did cooking, etc, but he did the fetch and carry duties and room father duties. I had to accept that the kids were much more familiar with him than me, especially as an OB doctor." Helene named herself as the disciplinarian and noted that the children would run to their father for support. In raising their children, the Berrien Center Bible Church was the center of their social activities. The family attended together and prayed together, three services on Sundays and one on Wednesdays. One son had a perfect attendance record for which the church made a special badge for him.

Although Helene is semi-retired now, she continues to work doing admission physicals for a skilled nursing facility/nursing home in the Lakeland System. She enjoys the work but looks forward to total retirement once her replacement can be hired. She loves being with her grandchildren, playing with them, doing craft projects, and fixing their toys. She and her husband work with a charity in Florida that constructs bicycle-like carts for disabled people in Africa. The carts provide mobility for people with no use of their legs and up to one useless arm. Helene noted with pride that these gifts of mobility can restore self-respect and productivity to persons who otherwise would be shunned and despised. Helene showed me a small model she made of these carts and became quite animated as she exclaimed, "They change peoples' lives!" Helen continues to give weekly help to a ninety-three-year-old woman whom she initially met when volunteering for "Meals on Wheels." As throughout her career, her focus remains on strategies to help others.

The women in this study are children of war, the years of their births rooted in the history surrounding World War II. Their families faced the conflagration extending from Europe to America to Asia that marked them forever. For many, the parents' trauma of WWII lived on in the lives of their children in ways only revealed over time. One aspect of this fifty-year follow-up is the belated appreciation of the significance of the legacy of the Holocaust, of the internment of Americans of Japanese descent, and of the geopolitical consequences of war—China's civil war and the Vietnam War—on the women physicians in this project.

When Marie and Helene began medical school at UCSF in 1967, no two women in our class were less alike. To be sure, they shared with their classmates the attributes of high intelligence, an interest in science, and a general desire to have a profession that each considered worthwhile and of benefit to others. But in terms of their personalities and appearances, they were polar opposites. The warmth of Marie's personality radiated from her. It was inescapable immediately. She was feminine in a flower child, bohemian way with long skirts and wavy untamed hair. Marie became beautiful the moment she spoke or laughed. Not so for Helene. The roulette of DNA selection had not dealt kindly with her. Unhappiness with a modicum of anger pervaded her persona—withdrawn, unapproachable, quiet, probably shy, hostile. By her own admission, she viewed herself as unworthy of any attention or praise. Warmth and openness in personality cast a halo of advantage that attracts like a magnet, an electric force-field that invites acceptance from other people, Faraday's Law in another form. Helene remained out of its field. Yet Marie and Helene had more in common than they, or any of us, knew at the time. They shared the Holocaust, and in their careers, they shared a dedication to helping the poor, the broken, the underserved.

Despite their similarities in history and ultimate career trajectory, Marie and Helene were markedly different in two respects: first, they differed in their family's social and economic status; and second, they differed in their own abilities to express their feelings. Here the difference is night and day.

Marie described her parents as supportive and loving in their relationship with each other and with their two children in her interviews with Lillian. Indeed, Marie enjoyed extraordinary closeness with her parents, especially with her mother who was a remarkably warm and loving person. Marie grew up in an environment rich in encouragement and interaction. She had many friends. She was attractive and comfortable as a woman. Her interests were broad and encompassed music, art, dancing, gardening, and cooking. She loved adventure and was willing to take risks. It was no surprise that Marie had a happy, optimistic outlook and found great pleasure in her life.

Helene's childhood, by contrast, was lonely with no perceived parental love or encouragement. The self-reliance expectations of her parents demanded that she work to finance her way through college and medical school, which she did with no outside help or scholarship. She lacked the warmth and openness that invited friendships. In high school, she attempted suicide. One single moment of kindness from her father—when he said he was proud of her at her graduation from medical school—shined in Helene's memory as her peak experience in life. It was a crumb of emotional nourishment that maybe saved her. She felt love for the first time. She then spent the remainder of her life trying to capture love from patients and colleagues and the family she established. Despite all odds, she succeeded.

The psychology literature at the time of Lillian's initial study in 1967-1970 identified socioeconomic status (SES) as a major determinant of success in life. Now it is called having the right zip code. Regardless, it is the same thing—being born into the right family, in the right place, at the right time. In this study, the class background (SES rating) for each of the participants was based on the educational level of the parents.[13] Level 3 was assigned if one or both parents had a graduate or professional degree, level 2 if at least one parent had attended or graduated from college, and level 1 if neither parent had attended college. The rating does not correlate with the intelligence of the parent. Rather, it rates the economic success of the family. It also correlates with the exposure of the family to situations that often are more readily available to people with higher incomes—such as greater exposure to music, art, literature, high-income styles of living—and the ability to feel comfortable in those situations. Social scientists identify this relative comfort of higher income people as cultural capital. Lillian and her colleagues found that the class background of the physicians' families also correlated with their physical and mental health at midlife.

Although from a family of relatively modest income, Marie was enveloped in cultural capital. She played the piano and flute, she danced and painted. She had traveled in Europe and throughout Canada. She spoke French fluently. Her *joie de vivre* was clear as day.

Helene was starved for any clues which might help her understand and feel comfortable with people who had "inside information" conferred by cultural capital. It is a hierarchy impossible for most people raised without it to breach. What is remarkable is that she found a way to be professionally useful and emotionally fulfilled within the confines of the limited and hostile world she combated throughout her early life. She was comfortable with those who shared the communities she knew—immigrant, low income, disadvantaged—African American women and migrant farm laborers of rural Michigan. They shared her absence of cultural capital. And they in turn expressed their gratitude to her. Her quiet and modest husband shared her low SES background but not Helene's higher level of professional education.

The missionary surgeons of the Southwestern Medical Clinic, attuned to and comfortable with the kind of background that Helene had, directed their missionary focus on Helene with the intensity of a Sidewinder missile to save her from her bleak life. In their worldview, this meant converting her to their brand of Christianity. It became their project, their mission, ultimately their success. Once converted, Helene barracked herself in this protected environment and, within it, served her target population nobly. As she had driven herself without mercy throughout college and medical school, she did the same in her OB practice—15,000 deliveries over forty-two years in rural Berrien County! In return, Helene asked only to be loved for herself.

By the dawn of the twenty-first century, things fell apart for Helene in her professional world. The economics of medical care changed in Berrien as it did throughout the country. With the mergers of Berrien Hospital and SWMC into the larger Lakeland medical system, rules and medical bureaucracy invaded Helene's professional life. Helene fought back. She turned to sabotage. She wrote "family restroom" on the bathroom door to defy the nurses when they tried to hijack the handicap bathroom and subsequently had to appear before the professional conduct committee for doing so. She felt disrespected when defied. Lakeland's mandate to practice team medicine was the final malediction. She judged the new system inadequate, imperfect, substandard. She left.

Although from a privileged perspective, one which I probably hold, Helene worked within a rigidly circumscribed, black-and-white world—a world where her professional choices never would be questioned, where she made the rules, where she was rewarded in love, and where no economic motive predominated. Yet in our interview, I was impressed with her accomplishments. She did improve the medical world within which she functioned. She worked very hard and was innovative. I admire her. Hostility entered when systems of health care—without her permission or participation—changed around her.

Again, Helene's psychological inventory would have predicted the outcome. She had one of the lowest scores in "social presence" Lillian had ever identified. Lillian noted "she is shy and avoids contact with others, expecting rejection and ridicule, yet at the same time is responsible and can conform to rules and regulations." Her personality traits remained consistent. In the 1990 tests, on the Q sort, she conformed to Factor 3: critical, skeptical, self-defensive, over-controlled, keeps others at a distance.

To me, her life seemed narrow. To her, it was her protected universe. In the end, she judged her life to be close to ideal and that she had received the important things in life that she wanted. She pretty much agreed that if she could live her life over, she would change almost nothing—but with an important exception. Helene wrote to me, "I do believe my life would have been different if I had been more tolerant of imperfections in life and people. There would have been less painful conflict. I have come a long way since becoming a Christian, but still tainted by my upbringing."

That Marie triumphed in life was no surprise. The charm of her personality invited success. Yet the arena in which she chose to work was remarkably similar to that of Helene. From the beginning, even in medical school, she aligned with the fringes of society. In her last year at UCSF, she worked at the Women's Prison in San Francisco giving medical and psychological support to prisoners. She participated in the organizational phase of the Mission Rebels Health Clinic, a late-1960s organization serving marginalized communities in the Mission and Haight-Ashbury districts in San Francisco. While still in her residency at the Beth Israel Hospital, she transferred her focus to the elderly and disabled populations in low income and neglected areas of Boston. Tragically, we cannot have Marie's own words as testimony for her decisions, but we do have the insights of her husband and her brother.

The ravages left by WWII and the unimaginable horrors of the Holocaust formed the backdrop of Marie's earliest memories. Though the Feldheims-turned-Feltins found physical security in Montreal, they never felt safe. For years, they disguised their identity as Jews. From childhood, Marie and her brother never mentioned it. Like secret spies on the unwounded world, their life at home was undercover. Marie kept their secrets for decades, until she was almost forty, when the survival of her lineage became assured with the birth of her son. Some wondrous mixture of the legacy of her family's history and her basic generosity toward people led Marie to work with the frail and disabled, underserved populations of Boston. Where others might see broken lives, Marie saw people in a struggle to maintain their independence and self-respect. She volunteered to be a soldier with them.

Japanese Internment

The women in this study carrying a family history of the Holocaust were not alone in bearing a legacy of generational trauma from World War II. For some of their peers, ordeals at home in the US left a family history of anguish and often humiliation. Three women of Japanese ancestry in the group bore such scars. When President Roosevelt signed Executive Order 9066 in February of 1942, the internment of US residents of Japanese ancestry began immediately. The vast majority were American citizens. The order applied to the entire West Coast which had been deemed a military area. Although most of the internment camps were in California, some were scattered as far east as Colorado, Utah, Wyoming, Arizona, and even Arkansas.

One American woman of Japanese ancestry was in each class of the study. Three shared stories of their backgrounds with Lillian or me.

Tomoko Inadomi Hooper was born in the Tule Lake internment camp, officially the Tule Lake War Relocation Center, situated in Siskyou County on the northern edge of California near the tiny town of Tule Lake, population 785 in 1940.[14] Located to the south of the town, the camp became the largest incarceration site for Japanese Americans and Japanese alien residents during the war with over 18,000 internees. It proved the most controversial. The Tule Lake region, in general, became an incarceration hub. As the war wore on, Italian and German prisoners of war were held in separate facilities located on the western edge of town.

Tomoko's parents, Kusuo and Haruko Inadomi, were native-born Americans who lived in the San Francisco Bay Area when the war upended their lives. The Tule Lake camp's barbed-wire perimeter initially boasted six guard towers but, by the time of Tomoko's birth, twenty-eight towers dotted the fence, each tower manned by guards who watched the inhabitants. During the war, the camp transformed into a segregation center where people of Japanese ancestry who were deemed "disloyals" were added to the initial population. With the newcomers, camp security measures expanded to include a battalion of military police with armored cars and tanks as did the escalation of the overall hardship of internment.

In her conversations with Lillian in 1990, Tomoko said that everything she is today did not come from being a physician but "from being born in a concentration camp." The twists and turns of Tomoko's interesting life and successful professional career are described in detail in Chapter 7, Alternate Career Pathways.

When I interviewed Kathy Yamaguchi, she initiated her personal history with her parents' freedom from the Amache internment camp. Her

Kathy Yamaguchi, 1971,
courtesy of Kathy Yamaguchi

(Below) Kathy Yamaguchi and family, recently, courtesy of Kathy Yamaguchi

first words were, "When World War II ended, I think my parents wanted to celebrate and have a child. I was their celebration child."

Both of her parents were born in the United States, her mother in Seattle, Washington, and her father in Alhambra, California, though both sets of grandparents immigrated to the US from Japan. Her parents married in 1941. By August of 1942, they found themselves uprooted from Los Angeles and interned together at the Granada War Relocation Center.[15] The residents called it *Amache*, named for Amache Ochinee Prowers, the daughter of a Southern Cheyenne Tribal chief and a cultural mediator in early Colorado territorial history. The camp, located in southwestern Colorado, was in Prowers County on land mostly confiscated from local ranchers for the purpose of building the detention facility. Of the ten relocation camps, Amache was the smallest with a peak population of 7,318. Like Tule Lake, barbed wire and guard towers defined its perimeter. Most of the family of Kathy's mother were also imprisoned at Amache.

What lives in Kathy's mind is the aftermath of internment. Her parents, maternal grandparents, two aunts, an uncle, and Kathy—all eight of them—lived together in a two-bedroom house in Los Angeles on 36th Street. Actually they thought themselves fortunate. They managed to buy the house amid a housing market in which most sellers refused to deal with buyers of Japanese ancestry. Later they moved again to a home inside a red-lined area where they were grateful to their African American neighbors who welcomed them.

Kathy's parents managed with good success to build a stable life for Kathy and her younger brother who was born in 1949. Her father became a gardener as well as the owner of apartments which he rented as an additional source of income. But in thinking back over her early years, the prejudice against Japanese Americans, and against African Americans, remains vivid in her memory.

Joyce Yano was born in the Topaz War Relocation Center near Delta,

Utah, an internment site mainly for Japanese Americans from the San Francisco area.[16] Her mother, an American of Japanese ancestry, was born in Berkeley; her father was *Issei*, originally from Japan, and therefore barred from US naturalization until the McCarran Walter Act of 1952 struck down race as the basis of citizenship. The Topaz camp sat at a desolate site 4,580 feet above sea level in the Sevier Desert where wind and sandstorms blew through the uninsulated barracks only partially finished when the camp opened in September of 1942. As in other camps, barbed wire rimmed the perimeter and watch towers stood every quarter mile. Despite the harsh environment, the inmates turned to farming and managed well enough to be self-sufficient in food.

Joyce's mother entered the Topaz camp directly from the Tanforan Assembly Center in 1942. Her father followed by a more circuitous route. Initially he was classified as an enemy alien and imprisoned at Fort Sam Houston in San Antonio, Texas, a victim of the double suspicion cast by his birth and childhood in Japan and his employment at the Japanese Embassy after graduation from college. In fact, the Japanese Embassy was one of the few places where he could find employment. While incarcerated in San Antonio, he volunteered in 1943 to join a work gang composed of Japanese prisoners that was sent to Idaho to work on the western portion of the old Lewis and Clark Highway, now US Highway 12, that headed out of Idaho at Lewiston and into Washington State. Only later, after the end of the war, was the purpose of the highway improvement recognized. It was to support surface access to the Hanford Nuclear Reservation, the epicenter of plutonium production as part of the Manhattan Project, a covert stop on Highway 12 in 1943.

After the road work ended and with suspicion about his loyalty to the US dispelled, Joyce's father was assigned to Topaz where his brother was interned. He immediately met Joyce's mother, the camp's registrar. They married at Topaz, but Joyce's father did not stay at the camp for long.

He again volunteered for defense efforts. In 1944, he joined the Office of Strategic Services (OSS), the precursor organization to the Central Intelligence Agency, and worked initially in Washington, DC, at Langley. Later he was assigned to secret missions in India, China, and Australia. Though he returned to the West Coast briefly, he stayed in Asia after the surrender of Japan and subsequently worked as a translator in Japan for the Allied occupying forces led by General Douglas MacArthur. Joyce and her mother joined him there in 1946 and lived near Tokyo until 1949 when her father's government work ended.

After returning to the US, Joyce and her family lived in Berkeley in the poorer side of town and where they felt welcomed by the Black community. She attended college at UC Berkeley. During her childhood, Joyce remembered the Japanese community sticking together such that most of their family friends were Japanese. They had Topaz reunions frequently in the Bay Area, not in bitterness but in recognition of their shared history. The Topaz Museum Board, formed in 1991, eventually purchased most of the land of the camp site. It became a National Historic Landmark in 2007. Though she had been to the site in 2000, Joyce, with her mother and one of her brothers, returned for the National Park Service opening ceremony in 2007.

Moonlight Over Topaz

As I wrote this chapter on internment, with the full knowledge that my outsider status precluded my ability to comprehend the depth of injustice Order 9066 inflicted on the Japanese community, I happened to be watching the PBS series on *The National Parks: America's Best Idea* by Ken Burns. In particular, *Episode Five: 1933-1945 Great Nature* stood out. The episode title of *Great Nature* initially seemed odd to me.

At the Topaz camp in her capacity as the camp registrar, Joyce Yano's

Moonlight Over Topaz, by permission of the Estate of Chiura Obata, the image courtesy of the Franklin D. Roosevelt Presidential Library and Museum (watercolor on silk)

mother knew about Chiura Obata, an artist from Berkeley and, in the context of the camp, one of its famous members.

Obata[17] traveled from Japan to the US in 1903 when he was eighteen and already trained in traditional techniques of Japanese painting. In his new home in California, he intertwined his Japanese aesthetic with the grandeur he saw in the landscape of the West, especially in Yosemite and Yellowstone National Parks. Of his first trip to Yosemite, he said, "This experience was the greatest harvest for my whole life and future painting." It was foundational to his visual and spiritual inspiration. He called his paintings of the national parks *dai-shizen*, "great nature." His career flourished. He became well-known for his distinctive style of art, a respected and sought-after art teacher, and a valued professor and colleague in the Art Department at UC Berkeley.

Then came Pearl Harbor and Executive Order 9066.

Chiura and Haruko Obata were ordered first to the Tanforan Assembly

Center, then to Topaz. Obata continued to paint and draw in both locations. He did hundreds of pen and ink sketches of internment to capture the "grim dignity of the disabused" and bear witness to the harsh reality. As Cirrus Wood wrote in *California Magazine*, Obata also found beauty in the enormous bleakness of the war camp.[18] His art, more clearly than words, rendered testimony to camp life.

In January of 1942, the Japanese American Citizens League presented *Moonlight Over Topaz, Utah*, a watercolor on silk painting by Obata, to Eleanor Roosevelt in appreciation of her concern and sympathy for the incarcerated people of Japanese ancestry during the war and her disapproval of the executive order that established internment. The painting hung for many years in her bedroom. After her death, it was transferred to hang in the Franklin Delano Roosevelt Presidential Library. The haunting scene depicts ground fog rising from bleak and barren land, partially obscuring—or maybe dissolving—a barbed wire fence that leads toward incarceration huts and a guard tower. Fog continues to mountains in the distance, separates land and sky, and rises to blur a pale full moon. Obata often used the moon in his painting as a symbol of calm.

In telling the story of our national parks, the PBS series emphasizes several points. The establishment of national parks was an original and uniquely American idea. From the beginning, the parks belonged to the nation and therefore jointly to all the people. And the parks served as a unifying force within the United States as a place where people, from all parts of the nation and of diverse social, economic, and ethnic backgrounds, mixed together on equal footing. The parks welcomed everyone—citizens, immigrants, and visitors from abroad.

In his person and his painting, Obata symbolized the paradox of American idealism and reality. Our best idea in the form of national parks became Obata's spiritual inspiration. Our worst ideas of racial and ethnic separation and suspicion became his reality. His painting exemplified this circuitous, contradictory route of American history. President Roosevelt signed Executive Order 9066 and *Moonlight Over Topaz* now hangs in his presidential library and museum. The histories of others intertwine also. Joyce Yano's father performed defense work throughout his incarceration and internment, and he even continued it after the end of the war. Tomoko Hooper, born in the Tule Lake camp, devoted her professional career to the study of the epidemiology of harmful exposures to which members of the US military are subjected. Kathy Yamaguchi, the celebration child, marked the release of her American parents from Camp Amache. Thousands of *Nisei* Japanese men left the internment camps to join the US military in intelligence units and for combat assignments in North Africa and Europe. In fact, the *Nisei* 522nd Field Artillery Battalion liberated the Dachau concentration camp. And Obata's paintings of our national parks remain iconic symbols of our nation's best idea.

CHAPTER 4

CURIOSITY: THE ACADEMICIANS

When I watched my brother's slashed leg sewn closed and thereby decided my future profession, my thoughts turned to the mechanical—how wonderful it was that the equivalent of a needle and thread could solve this bloody problem so easily and, to my young mind, so elegantly that his seven-year-old leg would be fully restored. I liked the practicality of it. I did not ponder how it happened—why the jagged edges of the gash gradually disappeared into a crusty line and then a thin white scar. The busy fibroblasts, the most common cells of connective tissue, at work forming the scar certainly escaped my attention. But many years later once in medical school, the usefulness of what we were learning continued to impress me. If a newborn baby turned yellow from jaundice brought about by blood incompatibility with his mother, you just exchanged his blood to remove the mother's. If an abdominal aorta ruptured, you just tried to be quick and sew in a new segment of the vessel. If one's blood pressure climbed too high, you could prescribe a drug to lower it. The ways to solve problems were manifold. And, to top it off, the study of medicine provided a relief from pondering the impenetrable problems from college, such as Kant's ethical theory of the categorical imperative or the application of the Bolzano-Weierstrass theorem in defining Euclidean space. I found medicine within my powers to learn and, as a grace-note reward, so intensely interesting that it was a pleasure to study.

Today, fifty years later, I still love reading about medicine and will forever feel honored and grateful to have been part of the profession. I worked hard, did a good job, and earned the respect of my colleagues.

Yet, within the profession, there has always been that rare small number of physicians who become heroes, who take medicine to the next level either scientifically as investigators or educationally as teachers. As students at UCSF, we found mentors in both categories, some who received Nobel Prizes for their investigative accomplishments, others who became deans and honored professors for their clinical mentorship. With rare exceptions, our role models were all males. To be sure, the supply pool of candidate female physicians was meager. In my four years of medical school, I remember only one, Dr. Dorothy Bainton, who lectured us during our second-year pathology section. Her field included granulocytes, the white blood cells that kill bacteria, and specifically the little organelles within the granulocytes that deliver the *coup de grâce* to the bacterium. Attractive, relaxed, and no more than ten years older than I, she mentioned one of her children at some point in one of her lectures. Though we never exchanged a word, I could see myself in her—my sole, female-inspired, mentorship moment.

My subconscious must have worked overtime; I became a pathologist with an avid interest in blood disorders. Bainton went on to become a full Professor of Pathology, then Chair of the Department of Pathology (and the first female chair of a department), and finally Vice Chancellor of Academic Affairs at UCSF. And what is more, she became additionally famous for her involvement in a mystery from California's early, lawless, and haunting history. She initiated an investigation to locate the brain of Ishi, the last of the Yahi Indians, a tribe almost totally massacred in the mid-1800s.[1] Ishi emerged from the wilderness near the town of Oroville in Northern California in 1911 as the lone survivor of his tribe and found protection on the UCSF campus until he died of tuberculosis in 1916. Eight decades later, Bainton helped to locate his preserved brain, all but forgotten in a storage facility of the Smithsonian Museum. She went on to unite the brain with his cremated ashes to give Ishi a final and dignified internment in his tribal homeland near Mount Lassen.

Though I never knew her, one female doctor at UCSF remains in the memory of most of the women in my class as a mentor and clinical teacher, remarkable for her singularity, all the more so because she was still a resident only two years ahead of us in training. Dr. Faith Fitzgerald. She did more than inform. She inspired every young physician she met.

Medicine As A Mystery To Be Solved: The Sleuth

"In France or Japan, she would be seen as a national treasure," Lillian wrote to me with a note of certainty after her last visit with Dr. Faith Fitzgerald. Though I know Faith only through the eyes of others, it is not difficult to witness her through the descriptions by Lillian and my classmates who worked with her in medical school and in Faith's many publications in the medical literature, and, by providence, video and audio recordings of her in interviews and lectures. A computer search engine can deliver you Faith Fitzgerald "in person" on video.

But in July of 2017, when Lillian interviewed her in her office at the University of California, Davis School of Medicine, Faith seemed fragile. Her curly hair, that had never deviated in style from a close-cropped crown, had turned from brown to grey. Faith was seventy-four. As always, or so I deduced from photographs and videos, Faith wore only black—black slacks, black pullover and jacket, sturdy black walking shoes—with at most an occasional small pedant necklace or lapel pin. Fashion and personal decoration were not her thing. She sat in her small, cluttered office with walls adorned mostly by photographs of her many students from all over the world. They "risked everything to become physicians; they are brave and courageous," she told Lillian in noting the photos. I imagine there must also have been a photo of Faith with her mentor, Dr. Hibbard Williams, the physician in her life whom she admired the most.

Amid the piles of papers and videos and photos, a Razor scooter, of the unmechanized type that young children learn to steer before mastering a bicycle, rested against Faith's desk. After two hip-replacement operations, the second of which left her with extreme pain in her right leg, Faith depended on the scooter to navigate her world. She could no longer walk independently. Though her life was impacted by her limited mobility and failing vision, she continued to teach in a manner that Arthur Conan Doyle would have admired, a style that had remained her trademark from her earliest days as a physician. But her overall life is more a story that Chekhov might have invented.

Faith Thayer Fitzgerald entered UCSF in 1965 with a family background that rivaled a historical novel of aristocracy and revolution, mysticism and romance and was filled with archetypal figures belonging more to the eightenth than the twentieth century. Lillian narrated much of her story previously in "Medicine is My Lust: The Story of a Woman Physician," quoted in part in this chapter.[2]

As with other women in our cohort who emerged from the embers of the Holocaust, World War II, Japanese internment, Mao's China, or the domestic hardships of families hampered by the Great Depression and war-related disruption, Faith's family history from an earlier generation imprinted her. Her maternal grandparents belonged to the Russian aristocracy, to the "old Russia" of inherited privilege and czarist rule. Her grandfather, a member of the Imperial Guard trained in the Prussian military tradition, was stationed in Vladivostok when Lenin gained control of Russia. With the sure knowledge of death were he to stay, he fled with his wife and two daughters, first to Beijing, then Shanghai during the turmoil of the Bolshevik Revolution. These events led Faith's impressionable mother to imagine herself arising from a romantic imperial past and forging toward a brave new world future. Her mother's education prepared her for little of practical use: "a little French, a little opera, a smattering of the arts, and an abundant supply of dreams and fantasies" which she projected upon her intended migration to the United States. As a young and wealthy woman, she had surveyed the expatriates who roamed the Bund and the foreign concessions of Shanghai and settled her imagination on the Americans. As Lillian wrote, "Her glorious dream was to live in Boston, her perceived mecca of US culture; to meet and marry a tall and handsome Irishman; and to have two brilliant, beautiful, and successful children." For this, she immigrated alone to the United States in the late 1930s and managed to actualize most of her fantasies. She married a tall, handsome, charismatic Irishman who could weave music out of language and charm even the most reluctant and moved with him to Boston. But, also in the way of most fantasies, hers fell short. Sobriety and stability had been omitted. Her Irish bard drank "like an Irishman." As the United States entered World War II, she divorced her alcoholic husband and found herself alone and economically destitute with her infant daughter, Faith, and two-year-old son. But Faith's unlikely childhood continued. Ethyl Thayer, a member of the Brahmin Thayer family of Boston, found Faith's mother weeping with her two young children in an Anglican church after her eviction from her apartment. Ethyl Thayer gave them shelter and Faith her middle name. Later, toward the end of the war, her mother moved west with her young children to Berkeley, California, in search of a secretarial job.

Within a few years, her Russian grandparents left the turmoil of the civil war in China and joined them in Berkeley. Now, life for Faith reverted from the semi-destitute to the original imperial model. Her mother, with Faith and her older brother in tow, entered the household of her newly immigrated parents. In addition, a welcome degree of stability likely entered Faith's life at this point. Later, as Lillian recounted, Faith described it as like "living in an independent duchy in the middle of a large foreign country. Russian was spoken. The talents developed, the traits admired, and the values were Russian. The food, the friends, and all that makes up the fabric of daily life reflected the Russian ethos and imbued Faith with a sense of pride in being different from the great majority of Americans. She (Faith) perceived her family milieu as different but superior."

Without question, Faith's grandparents exerted great influence on her formative years. The communist revolution strengthened her grandfather's conservative bent and endorsement of the status quo which he would proclaim loudly, even to the point of having seen good in Hitler and McCarthy, endorsing them as men who defended law and order. Yet he had a "grand appetite for life," whisking the family off on excursions that felt big and adventurous even if the local library constituted the pinnacle destination. For him, the appropriate quest in life was to do something as well as you could without vanity, without trying to prove your superiority over another—but to do it with impressive style. He would say, "You should live life as if everyone were looking at you and taking example from you." His message was not lost on Faith; it became incorporated into her young DNA. "From him I learned grace, everyone loved him without envy. He did what he wanted without pretense but always with an air of confidence." Her grandmother, on the other hand, played the role of the imposing and dictatorial matriarch of the household, usually in opposition to the role of Faith's mother and her childrearing methods. The fray between her mother and grandmother positioned Faith as the prize between them. With a generous admixture of her grandfather's panache, Faith emerged fairly triumphant and credited her early independence and self-assertiveness to the imperial household fracas.

In concert with the other women in this study, Faith liked school, excelled academically, and grew intrigued with scholarship for its own sake as a way to satisfy her emerging and insatiable curiosity about the world. Her grandfather introduced her to the Sherlock Holmes books when Faith was young. Her ensuing fascination with them proved to be lifelong. Sir Arthur Conan Doyle based the remarkable powers of his Sherlock

Holmes character—powers of observation, deduction, logical reasoning, and conclusion from minute but key findings—on the impressive, real-life abilities in diagnostic medicine of Dr. Joseph Bell, one of Doyle's mentors when Doyle himself studied medicine at the Royal Infirmary of Edinburgh.[3] The idea of the physician as a hero who could solve diagnostic mysteries based on his acumen in following clues and deciphering the puzzle of subtle observations grew in Faith's imagination. She settled on medicine by age six and neither wavered from that goal nor ever doubted that she would become a physician. She too would become a hero. From another book in her grandfather's library, she always remembered a line from *The Egyptian*, a historical novel by the Finnish author Mika Waltari: "Before the physician, even the Pharaoh stands naked."

One puzzle she encountered as a young child was the disappearance of a few classmates each year. This was in the pre-Salk years in the late 1940s and early '50s as epidemics of polio swept through communities, afflicting and often killing children and adults alike. One vivid memory was a visit to a young friend's home where, upon entrance, the first sound she heard was a rhythmic moan. When they entered the next room, she discovered that the moan emanated from an iron lung that encased her friend's mother. For young Faith, the twin emotions of terror that even mothers could be afflicted by the disease and of the injustice of being so incapacitated stayed with her and reinforced her decision about medicine. In fact, in 1954 when Faith was in about the fifth grade, she and her brother were signed up by their mother to became "polio pioneers" to test the efficacy of the killed-virus vaccine developed by Jonas Salk. They thus participated in the biggest public health experiment in American history, funded by donations to the March of Dimes. Nearly 1.8 million people, including school children called "Salk kids," volunteered to receive the vaccine without the certain knowledge that the vaccine was perfectly safe. Jonas Salk became an American hero against the injustice of polio, and Faith could claim her small part in the triumph of conquering the disease.

Always tall compared to her classmates, she did well in athletics playing basketball, baseball, tennis, and hockey and followed "the tastes of a good Russian granddaughter in her pursuit of ballet, piano lessons, French lessons, and cooking." Her life at home was eccentric but happy. Though living separately and sometimes in different cities, her divorced parents maintained a friendly relationship and agreed that their son and daughter were "marvelous" children. Neither remarried. Her father quit drinking after the divorce and followed the family to California once the war ended. There, proving Oscar Wilde accurate that every saint has a past and every sinner has a future, he enlarged his zest for life to include a reforming crusade by starting many Alcoholics Anonymous chapters. As a teenager, Faith often accompanied him on Saturday visits to various AA chapter meetings where she would hear the participants relate their stories of addiction to alcohol and drugs and of their struggles and sometimes triumphs in life. The empathy and understanding that these stories engendered in teenage Faith remained with her throughout her career. She developed a profound sympathy for the underdogs of life that served her well in understanding many of her patients.

Faith's grandparents sustained a fairly prosperous lifestyle under the management of the grandfather, somewhat surprising as older immigrants almost four decades removed from their privileged past in Czarist Russia and pre-war China. But, after the patriarch's death when Faith was in high school and the subsequent inept management of finances by her mother and grandmother, the family's fiscal fortunes plummeted. Faith took a job as a cashier in a local theater. By sixteen, her income amounted to enough to support herself and additionally contribute to household expenses. Like many other women in this study, she managed to maintain an excellent academic performance and to work hard at a less-than-inspiring job without regrets. As she put it: "Work was fun, you met interesting people, and you had funds." These were prophetic words. From this early age, Faith found people interesting—even in the brief encounter of selling a movie ticket.

Faith differed from many of her female peers in her lack of interest in dating in high school and college. She had lots of friends and remained unconcerned about American dating norms of the 1950s and early '60s as rock and roll, recreational drugs, and hippies became popular in her hometown of Santa Barbara. For one thing, as the daughter of two very tall parents, she had "inherited their height and was always many inches taller than the boys her age. Because within her Russian home it was good to be big, she was regarded by her family as attractive."[4] As she said, "It was in the natural course of events that I was the way I was; I was not afflicted by concern for my physical being one way or another."[5]

Also, like other women in this study, Faith's academic excellence and hard work paid off. She won a Regent's Scholarship to college and entered the University of California, Santa Barbara, at eighteen. In addition to her premedical science courses, her natural curiosity about the world, no doubt aided by her unconventional background, led her to take many courses in the humanities: Baroque Art, Russian literature, Philosophy, and English. As Lillian recounted, "She had a nineteenth-century concept of the physician as a scholar and learned human being."[6] Early on, she abandoned on-campus dormitory living in favor of a private, inexpensive small cottage in Santa Barbara with a single bed and a hot plate for cooking where she could live as she pleased and study without interruption. She graduated as valedictorian of her class. The independent and assertive child remained alive and well.

Faith entered the UCSF School of Medicine in 1965, full of confidence from her initial interview that she would be admitted and certain that medicine represented the profession she was meant to pursue. Up to this point, she had managed to find reasonable, albeit slender, order in her eccentric life—grandparents clinging to an aristocratic Russian past, a capricious mother rooted in fantasies, a partially absent, previously alcoholic father crusading against liquor, and strained family finances that required her to work from an early age. But the fragile home regime collapsed as she entered medical school. Her father had died the year before. Her mother, now alone with both of her children away, her fantasies of youth, beauty, and choice in life unsustainable in the merciless face of advancing age, emotionally disintegrated. She was hospitalized. Faith's brother, in graduate school at Berkeley, had long since disengaged from family affairs and was soon to join the Marines. Faith became the lone responsible adult for the family.

Though academically successful, Faith had a difficult first year, perhaps the most challenging year of her life. She said, "I felt betrayed by the cosmos. It was difficult to love my mother the way she was, she had changed so, she felt like a stranger."[7] In her role as her mother's caretaker, she also became aware of the problems in dealing with physicians. The psychiatric resident treating her mother was insensitive and uncommunicative. Though her mother gradually improved and even went back to work by Faith's second year, the experience of her illness left its mark on Faith. She emerged with an increased awareness of the needs of patients and their families and a heightened capacity for compassion. "Before, medicine had been a highly cerebral activity; now people became vastly more important. The laying on of hands and touching people took on new significance, and (Faith) was determined to build her competencies and her capacity to be trusted."[8]

During her third year of medical school while on her rotation in the emergency room, Faith encountered the physician who would have the greatest influence on her career and who remained forever the mentor she admired the most. Youthful, energetic, with prematurely gray hair and an engaging smile full of warmth and enthusiasm, Dr. Hibbard Williams was the consulting faculty member called to see the woman lying on the gurney before Faith and the emergency room on-call resident. Their careers were in sync, in a sense. Dr. Williams had joined the UCSF faculty from Harvard the year Faith entered UCSF in 1965. Williams's manifest joy in the practice of medicine overwhelmed Faith on that first encounter. He combined a profound intellectual knowledge of medicine with the ability to pick up on small hints and clues from talking with and examining the patient to arrive unfailingly at a correct diagnosis. He was Sherlock Holmes combined with Sir William Osler. For Faith, the die was cast. She would be an internist on the model of Williams. And thereafter, and not by chance, they generally stayed in sync for the remainder of their careers.

Faith often told a story that occurred when Williams was chief of medicine at San Francisco General Hospital and Faith was the chief resident in medicine. The year was 1973. San Francisco General Hospital reigned as the medical epicenter of action in the city, the trauma hospital for the warring gangs, the accidents, the lost and forgotten, the poor and unwanted. Most medical students and house staff loved their rotations there where your help mattered and you witnessed life at its rawest. I know I did. The hospital, including its ambulance service, was under the purview of the San Francisco Public Health Service.

Each weekend the health service dispatched a van to pick up street people who seemed sick, mostly men prone on concrete sidewalks, often vomiting, or tucked into doorways, or curled over vents. The vehicle, termed the boozer-cruiser, delivered its clientele to San Francisco General Hospital where a room was set up with cots and blankets, a delousing tank, and waiting IVs with saline and vitamin B12. The genuinely sick would be admitted to the hospital. The vast majority were not sick. They simply needed a place to sleep and dry out. The next morning the hospital sent over warm buttered toast, hard boiled eggs, and coffee to feed the men, then sent them on their way in their clothes, washed by the hospital staff the night before. This was public service delivered with benevolence. The medical residents assigned to the emergency room prided themselves on being tough on this group of down-and-out individuals and tried to admit only the truly sick. They considered themselves to be the blockers whose job it was to protect their colleagues on the medical floors from inundation from gomers, a derogatory term for these unwanted patients later made famous in Samuel Shem's 1978 novel, *The House of God*. One morning when Williams and Faith conducted their morning review, an old, shabby, mildly hypothermic man remained on his cot, too tired to eat, not dressed for departure, merely lying mute with a helpless look of despondency. He had no medical issue that would keep him in the hospital, and the resident had written orders to send him out. As Faith described the incident in "On Being a Doctor," Williams said no, "admit him." When the resident objected, strenuously, and fairly demanded what the admitting diagnosis should be, Williams answered, "Compassion."[9] As Faith said, he suffered "the depredations of antiquity and abandonment." She again recognized in Williams the ethical values in medicine that she admired the most—to treat a person with empathy and dignity, that "the secret of the care of the patient is caring for the patient," and being the unwanted and forgotten in life was surely a malady worthy of empathy.[10] Echoes from stories at AA meetings with her father as a teenager must have resonated in Faith's memory.

After finishing her residency, Faith stayed at SFGH for a few years on the faculty in internal medicine, then accepted an academic position at the University of Michigan School of Medicine in Ann Arbor where she ran the intensive care unit. But that ended, in 1980, when Williams became the second Dean of the UC Davis School of Medicine. He immediately recruited Faith to join him as associate dean and member of the medical faculty.

Nestled in the flat agricultural central valley eleven miles west of Sacramento, UC Davis was founded in 1905 as a farm school for the UC Berkeley campus. Over the years, it grew in scope and importance to become its own independent campus in the UC system by 1959. Graduate schools were progressively added with the School of Medicine beginning instruction in 1968. After 1980, Williams and Faith remained at Davis throughout their careers, in sync, and created an outstanding and clinically oriented Department of Medicine in which the two physicians became icons and legends.

Faith's unconventional life came to fruition at Davis: the panache of a theatrical eighteenth-century presence from her Russian grandfather; the linguistic color and dexterity of her Irish father; and her own Sherlock Holmesian approach to diagnosis as a mystery to be solved. Indeed, "Disease is a crime," she would say. "It robs you of the things you can do, and sometimes it murders you."[11] The doctor became the sleuth. Faith's curiosity, ruled by an abiding interest in people and their lives, led her to ask as many questions as possible in order to understand the patient as an individual and to uncover whatever ailment brought that person to medical attention. She saw clinical medicine as stories of humanity. She taught students and residents with narratives about patients, unfolding mysteries that culminated in a diagnosis and treatment, or, at times, as solely interesting stories. She did it with style and grace —"as if everyone were looking at you and taking example from you," under the dictate of her grandfather. She would challenge the students and residents that everyone was interesting if you were to follow the clues to discover their story.

To prove her point one day on teaching rounds, she asked the residents to present the least interesting patient under their care.[12] They took her to an old lady whom they had dismissed as tiresome with no medical problem beyond failure-to-thrive from age and neglect. But she became fascinating under Faith's further questioning. The simple query, "Where were you born?" led to the fact that as a teenage immigrant from England, she had been plucked from the North Atlantic as the Titanic sunk behind her. This wizened, ancient woman then blossomed with tales of Iceberg Alley and life before the Great War.

When she was seventy and still an attending faculty member at UC Davis, Faith was invited to be the first physician to deliver The Last Lecture. This event was to become an annual address at Davis of the Gold Humanism Honor Society, a national society that honors students, residents, and teachers who embody the highest ideals of medicine in terms of humanistic care, compassion, leadership, and dedication to service. The lecture series was fashioned to be the parting narrative that the speaker wished to articulate about her role as a physician-educator as if this were her last message. Faith's lecture and personality were captured live and posted on YouTube.[13] In the video, she mounts the podium steps with obvious difficulty from hip pain and limited mobility, but, once standing on stage, hints of her discomfort evaporate. She appears as she always appeared— tall and thin, nearly gaunt, dressed in her trademark black jacket, shirt, slacks, and walking shoes with only a pin depicting Asclepius, the Greek god of medicine, as decoration. Her short, massively curly gray hair framing her smiling face, she launches with relish into her last lecture. It is witty, engaging even if the listener has no medical knowledge, educational for even an expert physician, and delivered as theater with the timing of a Shakespearean play—or a stand-up comic—complete with clever and whimsical power point animation. Her talk is a series of stories—tales of the people who had filled her life with their stories and taught her about humanity with its sorrows and triumphs, contradictions and similarities— with interwoven, unforgettable medical insights. As the thespian on the stage, Faith begins each anecdote as a serious professor with a description of symptoms and the diagnostic dilemma presented by the patient's case. She proceeds to circle around the problem, following a bit into blind alleys of medical workup, her eyes cast down in quizzical thought. Then a pause. Suddenly, she looks up directly to the audience, peering over the top of her glasses that had slipped partway down her nose. The light bulb flash. One more question is yet to be asked. And with her eyebrows raised and an emerging broad smile widening to reveal her dimples, she derives the answer to the final query that solved the case—*voilà*—an engaging story that ended with a medical insight no one in the audience would ever fail to remember.

Faith told the story of the man with headache, anemia, low platelet count, jaundice, and renal failure that no battery of tests nor history of work, exposure, or travel could explain until the sleuth asked the one overlooked question—*what hobbies had he?* His hobby turned out to be spending weekends shooting rats in the rice paddies of Davis, then hanging the rats by their tails along a nearby fence, and thereby generously bathing his hands and feet in mud infused with rat urine. And, as Faith happened to know, rat pee can be full of Leptospira, a corkscrew-shaped bacterium. The rat killer had Leptospirosis, a diagnosis that explained all of his symptoms. At the moment of diagnostic triumph, Faith declares, still smiling, "I lucked out." Far from luck, it was the thoroughness of her questioning and her encyclopedic knowledge of medicine that solved the mystery. Or, in another tale, take the woman in her sixties with a swollen abdomen slated for exploratory surgery, her condition thought to be an abdominal malignancy. Yet her arms and legs were also swollen. Moreover, she told the most off-color jokes and propositioned the young surgical resident in a hoarse whisper. She had the team laughing. That was the clue for Faith. She had "myxedema wit," a little- known consequence of thyroid deficiency resulting in brain dysfunction leading to social disinhibition. The abdominal swelling and hoarse voice also sprang from her low thyroid hormone level. Faith continued in her lecture with more than fifteen stories of patients who brought joy and humanity to her life. It was how she defined her career: the elderly women who were Holocaust survivors who came with chicken soup to visit "dabois" dying with AIDS;[14] the alcoholic Finnish sailor with bleeding esophageal varices who called her "cupcake"; Yoshi, a WWII veteran on the ward at the US Veterans Administration hospital who had fought in

Faith Fitzgerald, image from the
UC Davis School of Medicine

the Pacific and no one had asked "for which army did you fight?"; and on
and on, stories filled with the curiosity and humanity that Faith brought
to medicine. She recounted her life via these stories, her love of medicine
entwined with her interaction with the people she cared for and the access
they gave her into their lives. As she said, "I needed patients; I was dependent
on them for my happiness. They were my best teachers ever."

As Faith's sleuthing abilities became widely known outside of Davis,
she arbitrated other long-standing mysteries in diagnosis. At a UCSF
conference dedicated to notorious medical case histories organized along
the format of a clinical-pathological conference, the question of the cause
of the death of Wolfgang Amadeus Mozart became a subject.[15] Poison
from the jealous Antonio Salieri? Syphilis? Lead or mercury poisoning?
Over 100 possibilities had been entertained in the two millennia since his
death. Based on an analysis of the symptoms reported by Mozart's family

and physicians, Faith articulated her diagnosis of rheumatic fever from streptococcal infection with resultant acute nephrotic syndrome, now the most widely accepted conclusion from many different experts.

Along the way, in addition to the love and admiration of her students and colleagues at Davis, Faith received many awards reserved for only the most esteemed physicians: the American College of Physicians Distinguished Teacher Award, a Golden Apple lifetime academic achievement award by the California Medical Association, and best teacher awards from medical students at Davis. Without question, she found her greatest joy in life in her role as a teacher of medicine and as a recipient of the trust and confidence of her patients. In the many professional articles she contributed to the medical literature, her writing reflected her teaching with narratives of what she learned by listening to her patients.

Not everything was perfect. Faith embodied the nineteenth-century ideal of medicine in which a careful history and physical examination was of paramount importance, and laboratory and radiological tests provided only the finishing touches. The inexorable creep of technology, and physicians' over-reliance on it, filled her with dismay as did the shuffling of patients from one specialist to another without an internist assuming primary responsibility. As she so clearly discerned, the primary purpose within the design of the electronic medical record was to capture billing for each and every tiny bit of patient care and, for a given diagnosis, to require that certain tests be performed even if, in the clinical judgment of the physician caring for the patient, those tests were not indicated. Moreover, the electronic organization of the record was antithetical to the flow of medical problems and treatment. Everything was chopped into pieces, scattered without cohesion into bits of information that required a diligent search in order to be assembled into a narrative of the actual medical whole. Faith refused to use the system. The administration thereby docked her salary, basically cut it in half. Faith then retired.

The Sierra Sacramento Valley Medical Society has a podcast called Joy of Medicine which featured Faith after her retirement in October of 2019.[16] At the conclusion of the discussion in which Faith recounted her career and her absolute delight and satisfaction in dedicating her life to being a physician and teacher, I found her final note bittersweet. The narrator asked what had brought her joy in the last week. Her answer—it was her animals, her two old deaf and blind dogs and her twenty-five-year-old cat. Her heart remained with the underdogs.

Medicine Driven By Curiosity

A few blocks from the University of Chicago Medicine, the home of Drs. Rima and Evan McLeod is nestled unobtrusively on a tree-lined street of attractive older dwellings about midway between Lake Michigan and Washington Park. Rima had kindly invited me to stay with them while I interviewed her and then continued to Berrien Springs in Michigan to visit with Helene.

Until our forty-fifth UCSF reunion in 2016, I hadn't seen Rima and Evan since we graduated from medical school. Even then, in medical school together in the '60s, we rarely met after the first two years of basic science. Yet they were basically unchanged, still looking youthful in 2018, Evan appearing boyish despite his blond hair replaced by grey and Rima with blondish ringlets instead of her brown ponytail. "Rima and Evan" formed one word in my mind. They entered UCSF as a married couple and remained inseparable, aided by UCSF's nifty system of alphabetization for any class assignment purpose, no doubt adopted before the school could have imagined a married couple in the class. Evan cooked dinner for the three of us that night. I asked him if that was usual. He replied, "I like to take care of Rima." I thought, "what a lovely answer." And his dinner was very good.

Out of the fifty-eight women in the study, eight have had strictly academic careers. In our class of 1971, Rima remains the only female member to claim that distinction. In the next two days, I learned that Rima's investigative career could have been foretold; she is consumed by curiosity and empowered by perseverance.

As Rima recounted her childhood to me, I decided it must have been sprinkled by fairy dust and guarded by a sprite of light and happiness, an account of her early years almost unbelievable except for her unassailable honesty. I didn't know such lives existed.

"Where did I come from ..." Rima began in writing a short autobiography in 2009 for *We Were Fellows*, a book for Jack S. Remington, MD, the Stanford professor in whose laboratory she did her infectious disease fellowship.[17] "I was born in Berkeley, California, on September 14, 1945. My mother was a public health nurse, began and directed a nursery school in our neighborhood, and later made a program with my dad called 'Prison Match' that allowed children to be with their incarcerated parent on Sundays. My (physician) father worked in the US Food and Drug Administration for the twelve Western states and later directed the California Department of Public Health. My older brother was five and a half years old when I was born and was already a violinist playing with the San Francisco Symphony and later in Carnegie Hall as a teenager. My little sister was born two and a half years after me and was always a free spirit who loved to play and dance. My brother and sister and their families are musicians, dancers, teachers and bird watchers/listeners now. We lived in a house that my godfather, an architect, and my parents designed and built at the tip of the hill in Berkeley. It was surrounded by acres of trees, a stream, and a clear view down to the bay and over to the Golden Gate, San Francisco, and Marin County. I remember the house as filled with light, laughter and music." It sounded like a fairy tale to me. I kept reading. No wicked witch appeared.

And indeed, as Rima recounted specific adventures of her childhood, her opening paragraph documented her recollection as accurate, at least in her memory. She dug hillside excavations into forts with the son of a professional cellist mother and UC Berkeley philosophy professor father. She played with her friend Evelyn, whose kindly, older violinist grandfather was Albert (Einstein). She roamed the pathways of Tilden Park and Marin County. She watched her dogs and puppies playing with cats, kittens, and rabbits. She fearlessly rode her tricycle alone as a three-year-old to downtown Oakland and was rescued from Jack London Square by a policeman. She played the flute, piano, and guitar and danced and hiked and swam. She rode her horse bareback among the redwoods, unafraid to share the trails with rattlesnakes and Hell's Angels on motorcycles. "It seemed like the world was endless, beautiful, free and full of potential, and actually, so it has been for me. My family was very gentle and kind. My formative life felt very free, happy and sunny."

No dark memories of war or revolution, family conflict or death, poverty or ill health haunted Rima in childhood or her early adulthood as she matured into the quiet, seemingly shy woman who entered UCSF in 1967. Her family avoided conflict. She said it had been bred out of her. Her father let her mother make all the decisions. No voices were ever raised. In fact, to this day, Rima's voice remains soft, almost a whisper, inaudible in a room with ambient noise. She watched and listened in medical school, never interrupting but alert and ready to contribute if invited, smiling, her long brown hair pulled back and held in place with a band, her five-foot frame small enough that she might go unnoticed, sitting quietly next to her husband.

Evan and Rima met at Berkeley High School and there, while teenagers, fell in love and declared their intent to marry. Evan's older brother served perhaps as their cupid. He taught Rima archery (and tennis) in a summer recreational program when she was a child. They started college engaged

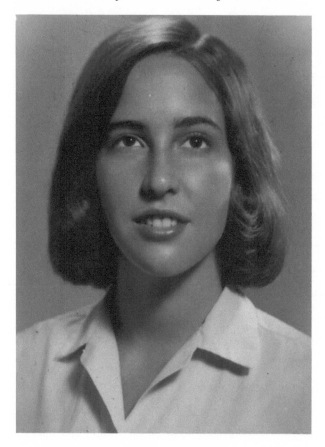

Rima McLeod, 1968, courtesy of Rima McLeod

and married soon after they graduated from UC Berkeley in her family's garden surrounded by friends, family, music, and sunshine with the Golden Gate glowing in the distance.

At Berkeley Rima had her first significant exposure to science, far surpassing her high school encounter that extended no further than chemistry. In fact, initially she thought she might major in physics, excited by the prospect of academic experiences with big questions such as the creation of the universe. Rima's fundamental description of herself was then, and remains, that of a curious person, full of questions, one who liked problem-solving and found it to be exciting and fun. Science, the problems and solutions that it entailed, were play, not work. Perhaps the many animals roaming the Berkeley hills with Rima in her childhood conspired in her decision to major in zoology. Her honors thesis was about the effect of light on the length of rods and cones in the eye of Xenopus laevis, the African clawed frog. This immigrant frog represented a non-native species outlawed in the United States but freely roaming as feral frogs in California, presumedly also in Berkeley, protected in the wild by the noxious cutaneous mucous it secreted in the face of danger. An attacking dog would throw up on first bite.

Though concentrating on science, Rima also stuffed her semesters with classes in English, French, poetry, history, and philosophy. An emerging desire to help people became entwined with her love of science and led to her decision to aim for medical school. She had good role models in her parents. And Evan agreed that medicine would be a good choice for him also, more as an endorsement of Rima's career decision than one he landed on independently. They applied to medical school together. Rima had liked college. "School was fun," she said. And she did well; she graduated Phi Beta Kappa. Importantly her undergraduate decision for medicine proved ideal for both her and Evan.

Five decades later as Rima describes her career, she repeats, "I just bumbled along." But far from bumbling, her career is missile straight, its target continuously in focus, and, to this day, its force undiminished.

In our alphabetized class at UCSF, Rima and Evan were a McLeod unit, together always, an attractive couple in a youngish and innocent way, seemingly undisturbed by the cynicism toward the government born of the the Vietnam War, the hippie drug and counterculture scene a few blocks from the campus, and the steady drumbeat of political assassinations. Instead, they made the most of medical school and found the best of mentors. In summers, Rima worked and made friends with young faculty members Dr.

Michael Bishop and Dr. Harold Varmus, UCSF's fast-rising superstars who shared the Nobel Prize in Medicine twenty years later for their discovery of the cellular origin of retroviral oncogenes. Rima and Evan shared a cadaver first year, practiced phlebotomy on each other second year, and rotated together in physical diagnosis groups as we learned the rudiments of physical examination.

Rima's experience in her group spotlighted the inappropriateness of medical school in the 1960s. In the section teaching the examination of the heart and lungs—how to use the stethoscope to listen to the rhythmic beat of the heart and breath sounds of the lungs—Rima was the only female student with a male instructor and three male classmates including Evan. The students were instructed to strip to the waist, that is, to expose their chests free of garments down to bare skin, in her case without even her bra. Next, they pulled out their new stethoscopes to practice on each other to Rima's intense embarrassment, consternation, resentment, and, no doubt, to the instructor's amusement. At one point or another, similar situations ranging from clumsy to callous happened to most of our female classmates in the four years of medical school.

Rima and Evan matched together for internal medicine internships and first-year residencies at the University of Pennsylvania, a rigorous program with call every other night, the usual drill for that era before reforms in 2003 began to limit work hours for interns and residents. After two years, they returned to San Francisco primarily because Evan was to take a position at the Public Health Hospital, a coveted and attractive way to avoid the Berry Plan physician draft that was active throughout the Vietnam War.[18]

The Berry Plan

These were the years of military conscription, now a matter of history, but in the 1960s and early '70s, a matter of contention that dominated the lives of young men, including young doctors, just as the Vietnam War in general ensnarled and split the nation. The Selective Service Act of 1948 was still in force and mandated that all men register at eighteen years of age for potential military service. For male doctors, their deferment for education lasted only to the end of internship. During the Korean War, most of the drafted physicians were fresh out of internship and served as general medical officers in Mobile Army Surgical Hospital (MASH) units. Not only did this form of draft interrupt further training for young doctors, it also left the military with minimally trained physicians and insufficient numbers of surgeons and other specialists.

After the armistice that ended the war in 1953, Frank B. Berry, MD, became Assistant Secretary of Defense, Health and Medical in the Department of Defense. A renowned and highly respected surgeon, Berry was also a veteran who had served in WWI with the American Expeditionary Force in France and as a medical officer with the Seventh US Army in North Africa, Sicily, Italy, France, and Germany in WWII. In fact, Colonel Berry led the planning for the organization of medical services for the Seventh Army during Operation Dragoon that liberated southern France in August of 1944.[19] He landed with the main invasion force near Saint Tropez that fought the highly successful battles up the Rhône Valley that likely saved the lives of Marie Feltin and her parents. Later, he was a medical consultant to the US Army in Korea during that war.

He was an excellent choice for his position. Few physicians could claim the breadth and depth of his medical experience in the military. Working with national medical organizations, medical schools, residency training programs, hospitals, and the military, he devised what came to be known as The Berry Plan. Of his plan, he said, it "would give the hospitals a group of men to continue their training and would provide the military services with men of different status and in different states of training."[20]

But during the Vietnam War, his plan became the dreaded Berry

Plan. It dominated the decisions of male medical students. On finishing internship, they faced two choices, Faustian to many: either proactively and voluntarily join the armed services, continue with residency training, and then go into military service, or take their chances with the selective service draft and risk going into the Army as a Private. A small number, with pull or good luck, managed a third choice: after some residency training, join an alternate government service such as the Indian Health Service, the Public Health Service, or the National Institutes of Health. Most young doctors "volunteered" for the Berry Plan and became Captains in the Army.

In my memory, the decade of the Vietnam War remains a blur of anxiety and disillusionment that blanketed every aspect of life. I thought the war a dreadful mistake and unjust to the Vietnamese and to the Americans sent to fight the war. As female physicians were exempted from the Berry Plan, some of us were secondarily involved because of the choices forced upon our male friends, boyfriends, even husbands. The soldiers fighting the war deserved the best medical care possible. I supported that—and the point of the Berry Plan was to supply the medical personnel to give that care. We could all support that intent. The dilemma remained that the war should not be happening in the first place. The crisis of the era and our participation in it imposed an exigency that forced some decisions that I, and some others, lived to regret.

The Berry Plan lasted until the end of the war in Vietnam. The Paris Accords, signed in January of 1973, ended the draft for doctors and civilians alike as it brought the war to its ignominious end.

When Rima and Evan returned to San Francisco in the summer of 1973, more dust of good fortune settled on them. The end of the draft and the closure of the Public Health Hospital in San Francisco freed Evan of his Berry Plan commitment. Together, he and Rima completed their residencies in internal medicine at UCSF.

In 1975, electing to bypass chief residency slots, they allowed themselves a year of adventure. They took off—backpacked in Europe, hiked in the Swiss Alps, picked up a Fiat in Geneva, and drove and camped across Turkey to Iran. There they joined Ashgar Rastegar, their friend and former chief resident from Pennsylvania, to care for patients and to teach at the Pahlevi Hospital in Shiraz, a city in southwestern Iran not far from the Persian Gulf. By then it was 1976—and lucky timing. Rima and Evan managed their stay in the last wave of Americans welcomed into Iran to this day. Within two years, the Iranian revolution would end the modernizing yet iron-fisted rule of Shah Mohammed Reza Pahlavi and irrevocably damage the Carter Administration with the Iran hostage crisis.

It was a transformative time for Rima and Evan. As Rima said, they witnessed Iranians "who lived in a fascinating blend of cultures—some modern, some very ancient and free for the nomadic people, some quite primitive and poor. We cared for villagers whose water for washing and for waste flowed through the same drainage ditches and trenches frequented by the wild dogs.... We cared for persons with many different infectious diseases and honed our clinical skills, recognizing what was most important without the benefit of sophisticated laboratory testing."[21] These experiences served them well throughout their careers. Likely fostered by this exposure to infectious diseases on an international scale, Rima's focus shifted away from thoughts of research on oncology-related viruses ("a specialty where I could not cure people, which was what oncology was at that time") and toward infectious diseases.

Upon returning to California, Rima accepted a post-doctoral fellowship in the laboratory of Jack S. Remington, MD, in the Stanford Infectious Diseases Program, and Evan returned to UCSF for a pulmonary fellowship at the Cardiovascular Research Institute. Rima's experiences at Stanford established her commitment to finding methods to cure infectious diseases through primary research followed by national and international deployment of diagnostic and curative strategies. This work is what drives her professionally to this day. For Rima, medicine is about "helping people, patients, in substantive ways, especially in identifying a clinical problem, doing research to discover a way to treat the clinical problem. The arc goes from bedside identification of a problem to bench research and then returns to the bedside in such a way to help the patients."

With their fellowships, Rima and Evan swerved apart geographically for the first time. They moved to Palo Alto to be near Rima's work at Stanford Medical School. Evan, ever gallant, accepted the commute to San Francisco to his fellowship in pulmonary medicine at UCSF. Rima was on her own at Stanford. Additionally she was the first female fellow to train with Dr. Jack Remington, Professor of Medicine at Stanford University School of Medicine and Department Chairman for Immunology and Infectious Disease at the Stanford-affiliated Research Institute. Dr. Remington, even then, was legendary as the "pope of toxoplasmosis," a world-wide parasitic infection transmitted from mother to newborn with devastating neurological consequences.

Rima's experience in her fellowship set the blueprint for her professional career, even to her selection of *Toxoplasma gondii* as her life-long focus. At the Research Institute, she learned the elements of rigorous scientific research. In recollection of those years, Rima said, "I am certain that part of the process he (Dr. Remington) thought I needed in that training period to be a successful scientist and physician was to be much tougher and very, very rigorous in everything I said. My approach was to work hard and quietly. I grew up in a household where one did not speak unless someone had something nice to say, and no one spoke above a quiet, gentle, and polite voice in my family. Everyone at the Research Institute was smart, helpful, and funny sometimes, ... it was quite an experience for me to hear the level of intensity in conversations there...and the language! It did make me tougher, but thank goodness for my friends ..."[22]

During her Stanford years, Rima solidified the rigorous and inquisitive foundation upon which she would construct her academic career. "Because of the freedom given to me in my work at the Research Institute, I think I became more confident and secure enough in my own imagination and ability to learn essentially any experimental techniques .... although the complexity of the research tools ... has changed ... I did not feel bound by a methodology or methodological discipline but rather found my work driven instead by the questions being asked and felt quite willing to cross scientific disciplines to answer those questions."[23]

In addition to research, Rima's fellowship included clinical rotations as consultant for all types of infectious diseases—bacterial, viral, fungal, and parasitic—within the medical and surgical services at Stanford.

Both fully trained and specialized, Rima and Evan began a new life in Chicago, leaving behind their deep roots in Berkeley and San Francisco, their love of the Sierra and the Pacific, and more profoundly, their families. To be sure, they stayed in touch with everything that united them with the Bay Area, but now they were two thousand miles away. Though Chicago seemed like an odd choice, the jobs were there.

Lillian could have predicted Rima's professional adaptation at this point. Shy, seemingly reticent Rima, whose voice barely raised above a whisper, who quietly watched and listened and spoke only if she had something nice to say, had a distinctly unusual psychological profile based on the many tests she, and all of the women in the cohort, completed as part of Lillian's study. She ranked in the top 7% of the women in her quantitative and science scores based on the medical admission test. In terms of personality, Rima's profile suggested an extremely well-functioning person able to perform independently and, at the same time, to take charge, to be psychologically attuned to others, and to embrace original and creative endeavors. Lillian rated Rima "in a class by herself" in terms of intellect, independence, and tolerance. In addition, she had the advantage of coming from what Lillian termed a "harmonious intellectual family" with educated parents, an intellectually and culturally stimulating home environment, and more than adequate economic resources.

Even with her inner strength and advantageous background, Rima's new life in the Windy City had a rocky first year which easily could have left another shipwrecked. The competing demands of career and personal life hit like a hurricane: a new home in an unfamiliar city, a Chicago winter of snow and blizzards, an administrative urgency by Reese Hospital to get her independent research project up and running by the end of the year, a six-month rotation on the infectious disease service with responsibility for all the clinical consultations, AND the birth of her first child by caesarean section with no maternity leave. Rima survived, but just barely. It took some time to devise a system to cope.

Her first child, Allegra Marie, was named Allegra from the Longfellow poem, "The Children's Hour," ("From my study I see in the lamplight, / Descending the broad hall stair, / Grave Alice, and laughing Allegra, / And Edith with golden hair") and Marie for Marie Curie. Allegra brought great joy to Rima and uncovered her natural maternal instincts. To have time with her young daughter, she would arise at four or five in the morning to play with Allegra before going to work at eight and return home for lunch as often as possible. In the evenings, she again focused on her daughter who would stay up late, a long afternoon nap having been inserted into Allegra's schedule to accommodate an adult bedtime. Rima hired full-time childcare help. When she was on the clinical consult rotation and unable to have any flexibility in her schedule, Rima's mother would fly from Berkeley to be with her granddaughter. Rima repeated this schedule seven years later when her son, Derin, was born.

Even with these adjustments, Rima found her life as a mother difficult. "I often cried as I left for work," she recounted. In order to cope, she compartmentalized work and home into separate slots, but it came out of her hide. It was she who suffered over not having enough time with her own children and the "golden sunshine and carefree play" she remembered from her childhood. In the end, though, she feels there was no negative impact on the children. The hardship belonged to her.

Lillian documented in her 1975 follow-up that role strain and career satisfaction were independent variables.[24] Some of the women delayed the start of their careers until after their children were older and in school. Others worked part-time. Yet others shared Rima's complicated work-around methods to soldier on, doing it all, with good executive function in hiring extra help. It is noteworthy that women from less educated family backgrounds lacked the role models needed for bringing in more help. So they chose to do it all themselves much to the detriment of their well-being.

Though Rima shared similar role strain with virtually every other woman in the group who had children, she also shared similar professional satisfaction. Her academic career blossomed, no doubt aided by her early start and continuous commitment to it. She directed her research to Toxoplasmosis, a disease she knew well from her fellowship and one that had substantial public health implications. The brains of 30 to 50% of the world population are estimated to be infected by the causative agent.

Toxoplasmosis is one of the orphan diseases that escapes widespread publicity, at least in the United States, but has devastating consequences. The nefarious creature that causes the disease, impressively named *Toxoplasma gondii*, is a tiny, one-cell organism that can find a home in cats, sheep, and other animals. From earliest time, humans have been plagued by diseases in this broad category of protozoan parasitic infections that also includes malaria, amebiasis, and giardiasis. Only a few of the diseases have known, completely curative treatments.

Toxoplasmosis is wicked. *Toxoplasma gondii* attacks the brain and eyes of its human victims. Quite by accident, incognito, the disease can be acquired by eating undercooked meat or oral contamination with the feces of infected cats. Once infected, a mother can transmit the disease to her fetus or newborn infant. Severe neurological damage including blindness, tumors, and other neurological diseases haunt the human outcome.

Rima's contribution to understanding and treating toxoplasmosis is immense. Throughout her career, her work has centered on the creation and development of medicines to cure toxoplasmosis and of a vaccine to prevent the disease in the first place. Initially, to treat young children, she and colleagues started with drugs that were known to be effective in treating other protozoan diseases. Success with these trials (that helped to protect life, sight, and cognition for those infected while in utero) led to the establishment of a large toxoplasmosis registry. This was a significant step. The registry, named "The National Collaborative Congenital Toxoplasmosis Study" (NCCTS) tracks patients and their mothers in a coordinated and well-documented, longitudinal study. The health follow-up of the subjects is in-person by a group of colleagues in different specialties in Chicago. The registry allows for the ongoing study of genetic and immunologic pathways of the disease and the development of additional drugs for treatment. And since the beginning, Rima has also advocated strongly for universal prenatal testing for the parasite which, when coupled with a vaccine, has the promise of eradication of the disease.

Rima continues to work more than full-time as the Medical Director of the Toxoplasmosis Center at the University of Chicago. She is Professor of Ophthalmology and Visual Science and Pediatrics, Fellow with the Institute for Genomics and Systems Biology, and member of committees on Molecular Medicine, Immunology, and Genetics. Her research, most often in collaboration with others, has had almost continuous funding by the NIH, a remarkable record, and considerable funding from multiple

Rima McLeod, recent photo, courtesy of Rima McLeod

foundations. She is recognized both nationally and internationally as one of the most successful investigators and best physicians in the field. And she has no intention of retiring. She said, "It's too exciting—I think we are on the verge of a breakthrough leading to a vaccine, curative medicines, public health programs, and the potential eradication of the disease."

Polar opposites if you were casually to meet them, like a kitty versus a lioness, Rima and Faith in fact possessed their most important quality in common: intense curiosity. As I've discovered in research for this study, everyone who interacted with Faith remembered her with awe—the pure energy of her personality, her warmth and obvious empathy for her patients, and the art of medicine she taught as mystery theatre ending in triumph. Unforgettable. Rima, by contrast, hid in the shadows, her whispered voice barely heard unless the room was quiet and you leaned in closely. Then a really big message all but blasted forth. Of all the women in this study, their names will likely be remembered the longest.

Few of us, male or female, in the UCSF graduating classes of 1968-1971, will leave a medical legacy. Most will be remembered as physicians who worked hard, provided good care, and remained a credit to the institutions that trained them and to the profession in general. Both Rima and Faith are among those treasured few whose accomplishments will last for decades long after their careers are over. Curiosity as a driving force defined both women—always asking the next question, and if that did not untangle the mystery, then the question next in line, never stopping until finally the right inquiry scored a hit. Never accepting an easy answer—or probably the first answer. It may seem straightforward yet it is a rare quality to be able to sort the easy answer from the correct one.

Rima dedicated her highly focused career to one orphan disease, little known by the general public but huge in its worldwide extent and morbidity. The only rational approach to control of the disease in humans is vaccination. If a vaccine is ever developed for global use and toxoplasmosis recedes into the history of medicine like smallpox, it will reflect the sum of the work of many investigators. Rima's name will be high on that list. Significant milestones in medicine are almost never the product of one person. Rather, they are built layer upon layer of advances by many contributors, and Rima never hesitates to credit her colleagues for their contributions.

By contrast, Faith is a legend in her own time as a teacher at UC Davis. Her curiosity centered as much on her patients as individuals— the alcoholic Finnish sailor who called her cupcake, the rat hunter who waded in Leptospiriotic waters—as on their diseases. But how long will she be remembered? Fifty years from now when a vaccination against toxoplasmosis is mandatory throughout the civilized world, an internet search will feature Rima's name. What about Faith? Sadly, in the twenty-first century, her style of diagnosis and treatment is being forced from the profession by technology and the business of medicine.

Yet despite their dedication, unique contributions to their specialties, and personal joy in their careers, Camelot had its dark side. In some fundamental ways, Rima and Faith were professionally mistreated. Though Faith made no comments about her salary level compared to her male colleagues, she did retire from UC Davis rather than conform to the university-mandated medical record system that placed financial remuneration as its organizing principle rather than patient care. Rima has been underpaid throughout her career. Whereas the salaries of her male colleagues ranged between $150,000 and $250,000 or more, hers never rose above a maximum of $105,000 (including her $10,000 clinical bonus), or $65,000 after deductions. Other instances of degrading policies by some of those in the university cropped up. Rima received no reimbursement from her department for professional meeting attendance. Nor did the university pay for her publication page charges, even in prestigious journals such as *Nature*, as it did for other faculty members; instead, Rima paid the charges herself from her small salary. Though she has not complained to the administration about this treatment, which is ongoing, she wishes it were different. Others have described her treatment as demeaning.

Rima also recounts many instances of discriminatory behavior against people of color, Muslims, women, and older persons. Though it is difficult for her to bear witness, she does not intervene vociferously in public. Instead, she quietly registers her objections and attempts to find effective ways to counteract discrimination behind the scenes. She doesn't wish to become known as a troublemaker or to risk her complaints eliciting a negative impact on her work. At one point, she said that her ability to fight back in unjust situations was bred out of her by her childhood of "speaking only if you could say nice things," while looking quietly for constructive solutions to problems. Such strictures of conflict-adversity have become a burden to her as an older professional in a world that manifestly contains injustices.

As in any marriage in which both spouses have careers, compromises arise. Rima and Evan have not been immune. Throughout Rima's career in research, she has bypassed opportunities for professional advancement due to family concerns. At one point, she could have moved to Galveston with the promise of $50 million to build a program centered on Toxoplasmosis and other neglected diseases. She had potential offers or was short-listed for being head of the University of California Infectious Diseases Programs or assistant director in the NIH National Institute of Allergy and Infectious Diseases. As they discussed the opportunities, Evan would not say "yes or no" to the moves. But they had been a couple for a long time. Rima knew Evan wanted to remain in Chicago where he had worked hard to build a practice. Her children were more direct. About leaving Chicago, they suggested, "you go, we'll stay." Rima viewed staying as "perhaps best in the end."

CHAPTER 5

CAREER EVOLUTIONS

Some women in the study tracked a straight line through the jungle of their professions. I did—as linear as a laser. Beginning in about the third grade, I focused the next twenty-four years of my education toward becoming a pathologist and then worked as a surgical pathologist for the next forty years. Simple and straightforward. Once I had my gold-plated certificate from the American College of Pathology in hand, it never occurred to me to consider another course of action.

Not so with others. Some of the women traced professional landscapes that meandered into unforeseen terrain. Bonnie and Schumarry are in that group of women who were open to changes within their careers and then had the confidence to define new professional paths.

Bonnie and Schumarry came from opposite sides of the globe. They grew up in families with nothing in common. They began their careers at diametrical ends of the medical spectrum, Bonnie in pediatrics and Schumarry in surgery. Yet each extended her career far from its point of embarkation. Each followed one professional step after another. In the end, each found a transformative role in healthcare.

Spiritual Evolution Within Medicine

When I saw Bonnie Vestal at our forty-fifth class reunion in 2016, she seemed a different person from the twenty-four-year-old I remembered from our medical school days together. Amid the activities, we had little time to talk, but it was evident that her life had changed profoundly. Only the highlights stood out. The positive milestones were her two grown children, a long career in pediatric oncology, and divorce. The frightening one—melanoma. At that reunion, I was still in a fog of grief over the death of my husband, Alec, less than a year before, but enough of the change in Bonnie penetrated to signal me that I should visit her first. Within a year, I resumed my efforts on this project. I contacted Bonnie. Soon I was in Boise, a mere 400 miles by plane, 500 miles by automobile, in either case, not far from Seattle. I had never been there before.

Bonnie invited me to stay with her in her new home that she said had come to her by providence, appearing for sale at her exact moment of need. It embodied what she desired in a cozy, mid-century, white clapboard house on a tree-lined street in an older part of Boise. She filled it with photographs of her children, parents, and grandparents, native baskets, plants, comfortable informal furniture, and books. We talked nonstop for three days. For the video-interview, she sat in her kitchen, her halo of curly white hair catching the light from her backyard, her beautiful smile unchanged from 1967. Her story was unlike anything I could have imagined.

When she tells her story, Bonnie divides her professional life into the first twenty years and the second twenty. In actuality, this division belies the gradual emotional, intellectual, and spiritual evolution which led her from a traditional pediatric oncology practice to a nontraditional counseling service that includes interactive guided imagery, past-life regression, and hypnotherapy. In many ways, the two halves of her career correspond to the duality of her character and personality. One side concerns itself with the practical aspects of living—earning a salary, doing the bedrock work of her home and practice—and the other side focuses on trusting the spiritual messages she has been able to recognize since childhood. In the cosmic sense, it is her spirituality that defines her life, a life that has been far from easy. Along the way, she helped many children through their journeys with cancer.

Bonnie's dysfunctional family bore a single saving grace: her parents recognized the value of education, perhaps surprising since neither had much of one. Bonnie's enduring life raft remained her education. Her carpenter father worked in the gritty shipyards south of San Francisco and, though eventually rising to become a dock master, he had not even graduated from high school. He worked hard and passed on his work ethic to Bonnie and her younger sister. Leaving home in the early morning, he often worked late hours depending on tide levels. In his mostly silent evenings, he read or watched Westerns on television and shared little of his life with his daughters. Bonnie's mother graduated from high school at sixteen and worked as a secretary until she had children.

Fortunately neither Bonnie nor her sister had a rebellious streak. They managed to function in the emotional vacuum created by their parents. Their father described their private education at a Catholic convent in Belmont south of San Francisco, for which he had to pay tuition, as his gift to his daughters, a gift that strained the family finances. For it, he held Bonnie and her sister strictly accountable to do their best in terms of academic excellence and future use of their educations to take care of themselves. Hard work, thrift, and family chores defined their home life. Bonnie's mother sewed their clothes and dressed the girls alike. Luxuries were nonexistent.

By age fourteen, Bonnie recognized that her mother was an alcoholic. She tacitly assumed the domestic chores of cooking, cleaning, and laundry—and thereby relinquished any vestige of a carefree adolescence. Her assumption of adult responsibilities was an unspoken expectation in this household, ruled by emotionally absent parents and a code of silence. If Bonnie or her sister voiced an opinion, her mother would reply, "Who invited you to comment?" Years later as Bonnie and her sister stood over their mother's freshly covered grave, her sister asked Bonnie, "Why did she hate us so?" Neither sister had an answer.

The kinds of domestic responsibilities that Bonnie assumed at home spilled over to her school life. Whenever she saw something that needed to be done, she did it. Beginning as early as second grade, if someone were hurt in the playground, Bonnie ran to help. If some chore were left undone, such as cleaning a blackboard, Bonnie did it, unasked, automatically. The warmth and kindness of the nuns became Bonnie's main source of nurture and emotional stability. As Bonnie told me, one nun in particular who encouraged her in high school repeatedly said, "You can be anything you want to be with your attitude of willing and open diligence."

Her convent high school, operated by the Sisters of Notre Dame de Namur, offered silent retreats for the students. It was during meditation on a retreat that Bonnie first had visual experiences that became a form of guidance for her. She saw herself aiding others, assisting children who seemed in a war zone. These early visions inspired Bonnie to devote her life's work to helping children. Later, as a pediatric oncologist, she recognized her profession as her spiritual destiny.

Bonnie graduated valedictorian of her class. As she gave her speech during the commencement ceremony, she located her father in the audience and saw tears streaming down his cheeks. This was the most emotion for her that Bonnie ever witnessed from him.

In 1963, Bonnie left home for Stanford University on a full scholarship. She admired the beauty of the huge open campus with palm and eucalyptus trees nestled in the then-pastoral Santa Clara Valley. "I loved all the walking and remember feeling strong and healthy during those years," she later wrote. "My family home was only twelve miles away in San Carlos, but the residential congestion on the peninsula was already evident then." She lived in the school's undergraduate dormitories where, amid her predominantly wealthy housemates, she felt out-of-place. Her homemade clothes, self-administered haircut, and unsophisticated background isolated her. She remained on campus the first summer to work in food services and housekeeping. When some people questioned how being a cleaning lady at Stanford squared with also being a student there, Bonnie replied, "I can fit in anywhere." She did other menial work to finance college similar to that of Helene in food service at UC Berkeley. And Bonnie found pleasure in being with her coworkers in the way Faith did as a movie theater cashier.

At Stanford, Bonnie first articulated her desire to be a physician. When approached with this idea, Bonnie's academic advisor, a woman, countered with the suggestion, "You should just marry a rich doctor instead." Undeterred, and unimpressed with that advice, Bonnie soldiered on through her science courses and the hypercompetitive atmosphere engendered by her male premed classmates. Her father's admonition, "You're on your own," echoed in her mind. She did allow herself the luxury of two quarters at Stanford's campus in Germany and courses in psychology which she loved. Bonnie excelled academically and earned junior-year Phi Beta Kappa.

Bonnie's social life at Stanford, however, did not excel. The only event of note occurred in the spring of her senior year. She and her housemates devised a social night in which the girls would invite boys to see The Fantastics in San Francisco. Bonnie invited Bob Vestal whom she knew from premed courses. He accepted and, for the remainder of the term and the following summer, they dated and developed, as Bonnie said, "a deep, solid friendship." Little could she imagine then how challenging this relationship would become.

Bonnie's years in medical school are difficult to describe without including Bob and his constant presence. She became his needs-filling object, a float to absorb his perceived mistreatment by the world. I, too, made a similar mistake—two women, smart in science but not in men. As Bonnie continued her story, I understood it all too well.

Bonnie entered UCSF with her $1,800 earnings from cleaning and food service at Stanford and a scholarship from the American Association of University Women. By contrast and with financial support from his parents,

Bob selected Yale School of Medicine. At that time, they had no agreement to attempt medical school together or even a commitment to continue their relationship.

Though the first few months of medical school mostly remain a blur in memory, I recall Bonnie fairly well. Her warmth stood out, her gaze direct above her radiantly beautiful smile. She seemed more quiet than shy. Then, before friendships in the class could really coalesce, Bob suddenly appeared on the UCSF scene after winter break. Bonnie disappeared. Years later, she shared her story with me.

To fulfill his desire to become a professor and win national acclaim as a preeminent physician and academician, Bob thought Yale for medical school would be a good bet. A desire to be outstanding consumed him— although outstanding-in-what remained to be defined. Something went amiss in New Haven. One night in December, three months into the first year, Bob surprised Bonnie by calling her on the telephone, long-distance phone calls then being quite expensive. He was distraught and depressed. He hated Yale. He wanted to quit medical school. He didn't know what to do. He was coming home. Bonnie, grounded in perseverance through adversity, fatefully asked, "What will you do?"

Unbelievably, he said, "We could get married."

And so it happened. Bob returned for the holidays and managed to transfer into our class. He materialized at Bonnie's side in January. They married in September, Bonnie in a gown and veil she made herself, Bob arriving just in time for the ceremony fresh from a backpacking trip. They became Vestal and Vestal in our alphabetized class.

The next three years at UCSF established a pattern that persisted throughout their married life. Bonnie did all of the domestic work: cooking, cleaning, laundry, grocery shopping—whatever was needed. I remember Bonnie mentioning that she ironed Bob's shirts and wondered, why, oh why could he not iron his own shirts if that was what he wanted? But Bonnie did not mind. She said the work provided a break from studying. She was okay with the arrangement.

Their marital problems at UCSF were something different. Bob studied constantly, much more than Bonnie. Yet Bonnie did better than he academically. After each test, a list of scores was posted on the lecture hall door for all to peruse. Each student was rated from best score to worst, from 1 to 135. Although Bonnie and Bob often had scores close to one another, Bonnie's remained consistently several points higher. This rankled Bob. Then Bonnie made Alpha Omega Alpha, the national medical honor society, in their third year while Bob had to wait until fourth year. The climax, though, descended at the end of our fourth year. Bonnie and two other female students were selected to be the nominees for the Gold Headed Cane award, the highest honor conferred on a medical student at UCSF. The award is given to the student considered by the faculty and their classmates to embody the intellect and human qualities that exemplify the most outstanding physician in the class. The fact that all three nominees were female was unprecedented in the history of UCSF and a record not to be equaled for almost two decades. Bob considered it an insult – to himself and to all the men in our class – his outrage untethered from the fact that the nominees came from his classmates, 90% of whom were male. Bonnie went to the Dean and tried without success to remove her name as a nominee. In the face of Bob's reaction, Bonnie recalled withdrawing into numb silence. Fifty years later as she thought it over, she said, "I married my mother. He was jealous."

For internship, Bonnie and Bob matched together at the University of Colorado in Denver, Bonnie in Pediatrics and Bob in Internal Medicine. The two years in Denver were exceedingly happy and professionally fulfilling for Bonnie. She found her "tribe," as she called it, of mutually cooperative, like-minded, highly competent "buddies." In her second year of residency, during her oncology rotation, she recognized almost immediately that this was where she belonged. Oncology required a wholistic approach to medicine. In addition to the expertise to treat complex malignant diseases, Bonnie possessed the strong interpersonal skills and empathetic approach focused on the whole family that were essential for the specialty.

Though Bonnie wanted to remain in Denver for an oncology fellowship, Bob's career required them to move to Baltimore. Bob had a two-year position at the National Institutes of Health, an alternative to the military draft of physicians during the Vietnam War. To his immense satisfaction, he had an assignment in pharmacology, a welcome change from his internal medicine residency which he had disliked.

Bonnie accepted a third-year residency position in Baltimore at the University of Maryland covering a busy, inner-city service that resembled a war zone. In her last year, as chief resident, Bonnie gave birth to her first child in February of 1975. Her pregnancy was complicated. She suffered severe nausea and vomiting (hyperemesis gravidarum) and third trimester contractions that required bed rest for three weeks before her son's premature birth. Despite these challenges, becoming a mother turned out to be one of her peak experiences. During her bed rest, she received a vision of her unborn infant as a grown man and learned his personality to be that of a kind and thoughtful person. She became eager for his entry into the world. His name, Zachary, which translates as "remembered by the Lord," accompanied the vision. With his birth, she made an intentional compromise with her career aspirations in medicine. Nothing in her life would be more important than motherhood. This revelation ushered in a new way of being a pediatrician for her with a more profound understanding of a parent's relationship with a child.

After two years in Maryland, Bonnie and Bob gladly departed Baltimore for Nashville and fellowships at Vanderbilt School of Medicine, Bob in clinical pharmacology and Bonnie in hematology-oncology. For the first time, they both loved what they were doing in the relaxed, friendly

Bonnie Vestal, 1982, courtesy of
Bonnie Vestal

atmosphere of Nashville. Their second child, Sarah, arrived a year later. With their final two years of training over, they departed Nashville in 1977, Bonnie now with board-certification in both pediatrics and pediatric oncology.

Bob's preferences dictated their next move. Although Bonnie would have elected a return to Colorado, Bob chose Boise in Idaho. There he had the possibility of building a clinical pharmacology unit at the Boise Veterans Administration Hospital, a position that came with an academic affiliation with the University of Washington. In this setting, Bob had minimal patient care responsibility and, in the end, developed a successful research program and achieved his long-sought position as a professor of medicine.

In contrast, Bonnie met a difficult situation in Boise. The city had a single pediatric oncologist who worked two days per week and otherwise stayed at her horse ranch many miles away. She refused to consider Bonnie joining her practice and relented only after Bonnie offered to cover her practice for six months without pay. Then, suddenly, she left the country for Dubai. As a result, the Mountain States Tumor Institute (MSTI) in Boise acquired the practice and hired Bonnie. The Institute offered Bonnie a starting salary of $16,000, medical malpractice insurance, and retirement and health care benefits. Although at a very low salary, the position provided Bonnie the status of being the only pediatric oncologist in Idaho and the freedom to manage her life. Bonnie accepted the terms. She took the job.

For the next seventeen years, Bonnie managed the juggling act of a demanding pediatric oncology practice while raising her two children and caring for home and family. She worked every day of the week, approximately sixty hours in a week. Her salary incrementally rose to $106,000 after fifteen years. Although undeniably a low salary for the amount of work performed, Bonnie maintained that the flexibility of how she organized her practice constituted an adequate trade-off.

Bonnie became well-known in the greater Boise community for her accomplishments and outreach beyond strictly direct medical care. To have colleagues, she developed a support system of oncologists in Salt Lake City, San Francisco, Seattle, and Portland with whom she could discuss difficult cases and obtain backup consultation when necessary. Public communications about the Tumor Institute often featured her. Since a practice of pediatric oncology inevitably must deal with fatal outcomes, Bonnie often spoke at funerals for her young patients, a task she willingly performed and felt contributed to completing the circle of the child's life. When a child was ready to return to school after cancer treatment, Bonnie frequently conferred with teachers and school administrators to help them understand what had transpired and to smooth the transition for both the child and the school. As there was no pediatric hospice care available in Boise, Bonnie and her nurse often did home visits with a dying child. These efforts were done without pay.

As Bonnie was in solo oncology practice, she was also in solo parental mode. Bob concentrated his efforts on building a clinical pharmacology unit at the VA hospital. Bonnie believes that her evolving spiritual awareness grew from the demands of her medical practice and family life. She developed methods to handle each moment, working with what was happening rather than fighting against it. She relied on techniques of mindfulness, yoga, and meditation to assist her. Bonnie had a spiritual certainty that she was not alone and that she had the strength and the education to handle her problems. In fact, she believed that the gifts she had received—her education and opportunities in life—would guarantee her success. Her problems included her growing estrangement from Bob and his countless complaints and frustrations. The question remained, however, when would the stress become too much?

Although her situation was extreme, Bonnie was not alone in juggling the conflicting challenges of professional and home life. Lillian clearly documented this as the mid-life dilemma of most of the women in the study—a demanding profession coupled with demanding home life.[1] For Bonnie, her spiritual practice was essential to her survival. During her first year in Boise, she had a gastric ulcer and consequently had to give up coffee. Her spiritual guide, a Native American elder, taught her to start each dawn outside breathing the cold air with her feet on the earth and looking to the stars for guidance—and to replace coffee with ginger tea with turmeric. She has followed this practice ever since—though resuming coffee. Each morning she looked to the stars for guidance and always received an answer by remaining open to a message from any source, be it a song, a comment, a memory—anything. "If you look carefully, the answer will come," she told me.

For example, when a family of one of her young patients asked her to speak at the child's funeral, she turned to the stars for what three things to eulogize about the child. The answer always came. Bonnie said that her need for a silent way to find help grew from her early silent life that modeled no process through language.

A difficult marriage cannot be overlooked in chronicling the career of any woman. I think Bonnie did what I did in my unfortunate marriage— she compartmentalized. The children were hers to love and nurture, mostly on her own. Bob simply had too little interest to be involved with Zack and Sarah. But for Bonnie, nothing on earth rivaled their importance. Bonnie carried the responsibility of family and home until it, too, became "too much."

The professional part of the question—when would her solo oncology practice become too much—crystallized in 1992. Bonnie was seeing a child with acute lymphocytic leukemia, a form of leukemia curable in children, and this child was doing well. Bonnie was focusing her attention on calculating the chemotherapy dose when she realized what the mother really wanted to discuss was the child's school situation. At that moment, a nurse entered the room to announce that Bonnie was already five minutes late for the next patient and that the infusion room was waiting for the child to show up for her chemotherapy. As the mother and child dutifully left the room, Bonnie felt she had accomplished nothing with the patient and mother.

"Any oncologist could write the chemotherapy order but not everyone could attend to her human needs—the need to dispel the fear that would empower the resumption of healthy, full-on life. Life during and after cancer treatment deserves to be lived with every ounce of consciousness possible," Bonnie remembered thinking. The ability to give this kind of care had been taken from her when the system changed to the business model organized by administrators who inserted patients into fifteen-minute slots. Bonnie resolved to quit in a year and that very day asked administration to find a replacement for her. Previously she had written numerous requests for more help. Now, she unmistakably realized, it would take her leaving for anything to change.

Bonnie became increasingly concerned with helping her patients and their families manage the fear inherent in a diagnosis of cancer and break through the limitations that fear imposes. For her, it was a higher expression of healing. She had given over eighty talks to various community groups about a more wholistic approach to health care, always emphasizing that after a diagnosis and treatment for cancer, the child and family do not return to their previous state. Instead, a new being and family emerge that must be recognized and honored, a "new and better life," she said, "with an unknown future." Bonnie also endorsed using alternative treatments that she learned from other disciplines—such as acupuncture, healing touch, hypnotherapy, music or art therapy—whatever helped to treat or enhance the new life that followed cancer. In the 1980s and early 1990s, this openness to new ways to educate the community and help individuals to overcome the fear of a diagnosis of cancer was unusual and innovative. Recognizing this, the Girl Scouts of Boise presented Bonnie with its *pioneering woman* award.

It would take more than three years for the Tumor Institute to replace Bonnie with three pediatric oncologists and one nurse practitioner.

Concurrent with the search, Bonnie became a student of Angeles Arrien, an American-Basque, cross-cultural anthropologist and author of *The Four-Fold Way*.[2] Arrien used what she had learned from the Basques and other native groups about health, healing, and ways of living that had integrity.

When Bonnie started, she had no idea of what she was getting into. Bonnie told me about her experience with trance-drumming in which theta rhythmic drumming lowered her cognitive resistance. The theory in Arrien's teaching is that theta drumming is congruent with the natural rhythm of theta brainwaves and produces a state where mental relaxation occurs and one is prone to the free flow of ideas without censorship.

In the session, the participants laid on the ground with their heads to the north in their (imagined) "spirit canoe" to invite their ancestors for help. "So there I was," Bonnie told me, "sailing down the spirit river, feet first. Over my right shoulder, my grandmother appeared and described in detail her experience leaving Yugoslavia alone as a teenager for an unknown new world but with the confidence that she could make a life. If she could forge ahead into her future, I could find a way of healing for which I had no model. A former priest appeared over my left shoulder to reassure me that I would remain true to myself. Even my mother, critical of me in life, nodded approvingly."

The experiences with Angeles's method left Bonnie with the assurance that she possessed the ability to strike out in a new career and a template for how to proceed. Her grandmother's message convinced Bonnie that she had something powerful and novel within herself that would emerge. "I never doubted after that," she said.

In December of 1994, Bonnie first attended the National Institute for the Clinical Application of Behavioral Medicine (NICABM) conference that offered certified training in a variety of skills: interactive guided imagery, energy medicine, hypnotherapy, use of intuition, and alternative and complementary therapies synthesized into a support system for traditional medicine. Among courses, she attended a multiday seminar on neurolinguistic programming, a process by which the language one used for a particular subject shaped the manifestation of it. For example, if a person is afraid, then language expressing fear as a challenge shapes the outcome differently than language expressing victimhood would. In other words, the conscious use of language can shape outcomes.

In the course Bonnie volunteered to undergo hypnosis. Under the hypnotic trance, she saw herself planting a garden with seeds she found in her hands, followed by harvesting a flourishing field of vegetables. This experience increased her confidence and courage. Within traditional medicine, there was no model for any of this. As in her spirit canoe, Bonnie navigated farther into uncharted waters.

Through these experiences, Bonnie said she found her "tribe" again—though it took until 1996 before she could completely exit her traditional medical practice. She understood that this departure meant leaving the security of her respected position in the medical community of Boise as well as the financial security of an income and benefits. At the same time, she considered her decision to transition from straight pediatric oncology to an integrated health practice to be the pivotal turning point in her career.

At her retirement party from oncology at the hospital, the CEO gave a toast recounting the remarkable work Bonnie had done in pediatric oncology. "It was no wonder that Bonnie was burnt out," he pronounced. "Quite to the contrary," Bonnie thought, "I've been through the refiner's fire. I have come away with the good stuff. It's a different kind of burning."

Yet the actual transition proved difficult. Many Boise physicians voiced skepticism of her nontraditional approach to counseling which was hard for them to understand since it was not aimed at people with mental health problems. Some thought that she had "gone over the edge" including her then-husband, Bob, who mocked her spirituality. Initially Bonnie had few clients in her practice. She co-owned a building with a diverse group of counselors and psychologists who called themselves Integrative Health Professionals. Worse still, she had no paycheck, no benefits, and considerable uncertainty about her new career.

The answer she received from daily walks and meditation was to learn as much as possible. She continued to attend the yearly Behavioral Medicine conferences but, ever cautious, she additionally maintained her medical license and medical education credits to ensure that she could return to a safer shore if necessary.

During the early years of her new practice, she did a three-year apprenticeship with Dr. Christine Page on intuition, which confirmed her remarkable intuitive capabilities.[3] Her practice gradually increased and, surprisingly, consisted mostly of adults facing life-changing problems and not just cancer patients grappling with fear.

Bonnie had long known that she should leave Bob. Even her children suggested that she divorce him. His complaints about his life and his criticism of her never ceased. When she received awards for her service to the community, he would mumble, "It's difficult to be Bonnie's husband." Finally, in 1999, it was too much. Bonnie divorced him. And then, almost immediately, she began the process of forgiving him.

In 2002 Bonnie and three others formed a new group, North End Wellness, and invested in an old building inhabited by a haunting "friendly female entity." One member of the group did acupuncture, another did massage, and another counseling. It was a wild time with drumming, men's groups in the evening, zen Buddhist meditation during the noon hour, yoga, patchouli in the air, and the scene watched over by a friendly spirit hovering nearby. It was during these years that Bonnie learned the techniques of past life regression and became certified to practice it by Dr. Linda Backman, a story in itself.

In 2010, Bonnie was spending six weeks alone in a small cabin on a mountain top near the Continental Divide in Colorado after officiating at Zack's marriage to Caitlyn. During that interval, by chance she attended a conference of the International Society for the Studies of Subtle Energies and Energy Medicine in nearby Westminster.[4] She became fascinated, in particular, by a presentation by Dr. Linda Backman on past life regression/soul regression hypnotherapy.[5] Bonnie had long been using intuition in her counseling practice and had previously taken a three-year apprenticeship with Dr. Christine Page on intuition and hypnotherapy. In her work with clients grieving the death of a partner, for example, she had been able to suggest ways to communicate with the deceased person by sharing her own experiences in intuition and hypnotherapy.

To become more knowledgeable and professional in the use of these techniques, Bonnie started training with Linda Backman for certification in past life regression. Within a month, Bonnie easily and successfully mastered the techniques, most of which she had already used without naming them as such.

In her counseling practice back in Boise, she added past life regression to her regular services. Many people availed themselves of this technique, people who had questions which eluded answers in any other way. Though some psychologists remained skeptical, Bonnie's previous career as a pediatric oncologist gave her credibility. Offering her psychic skills openly was another turning point in Bonnie's life.

By 2014, the owners of North End Wellness began to separate to follow divergent paths and interests. Shortly after they sold the building, it was remodeled into a birthing center. The new owner called Bonnie one day to report seeing a purple spirit in the house that seemed pleased by the new clientele.

Bonnie continued her counseling practice for one additional year at a new location until age seventy, retiring in April of 2015. Two days later, she received the diagnosis of melanoma on the right side of her nose. True to her spirit and nature, she responded to her malignancy as a challenge. It became an adventure. Without fear, and instead with the deep conviction that she could deal with the diagnosis and treatment, she felt that her whole life had equipped her. In many ways, her preparation was traditional and methodical. She selected care providers whom she trusted, amassed information on treatment, and established a support system with friends and family. With this foundation in place, she viewed her melanoma as a new experience.

Freed from fear, Bonnie made unconventional choices in treatment. Her melanoma was stage III, a stage in which adjuvant treatment was often recommended. But without definite evidence of residual disease after

Bonnie Vestal, 2020, courtesy of Bonnie Vestal

surgery, Bonnie declined additional measures based on borderline changes. She had several enlarged axillary lymph nodes for which some providers recommended surgery, but, because it was equally possible that the changes were reactive and supporting her immune system, Bonnie decided against removal.

In April 2020, she sent me a photo of her new carbon frame road bike with tubeless tires and disc brakes, propped against her garden fence, purchased in early March to celebrate her birthday. Providence guided her timing. As the novel coronavirus pandemic descended, the bikes soon became scarce as their popularity soared. Bonnie understood her birthday purchase as yet another stroke of good fortune, a signal to continue on her road to ever expanded adventures, age seventy-five and feeling great.

Business Evolution Within Medicine

As I maneuvered my rental car through scary Los Angeles traffic to interview Dr. Schumarry Chao in November of 2018, I tried to count backward the years since I saw her last. Twelve was my best estimate, two UCSF Class of 1971 reunions in the past. I found her condo building in Century City, an obviously prosperous, even glamorous, high-rise section of LA deserving of its millennial name. Schumarry and I had not known each other in any personal way during our four years together in medical school. I doubt we ever had a real conversation though I did remember that she had been crowned "Miss Chinatown" of Los Angeles in college. As it had taken a year of persistent requests to arrange our meeting, I was grateful she agreed but a little apprehensive. How would she react? The moment she opened the door to her seventh-floor condo, I knew I was in for a treat.

Though in her early seventies, Schumarry appears fifty—trim, beautifully groomed, friendly, alert, and articulate—an attractive woman with manifest intelligence. Her demeanor is that of a woman at the top of her game, in charge of her life, and quite satisfied with the way it has evolved. When she speaks, she sounds like the businesswoman she is. Her choices have been rational and the product of a person who, when presented with an opportunity, knows herself well enough to have confidence in her decisions that progressively veered in the direction of more business and less medicine. In her career, she began with organizing systems centered on emergency and trauma medicine, which then morphed to organizing the financing and delivery of health care for the University of Southern California (USC) and Security Pacific Bank, then to medical systems and contracts within a major insurance company, and finally to the pharmaceutical-brokering-octopus that manages drugs within the medical universe. Though these steps allowed Schumarry insight into all the tentacles that feed into medical care (and extract profit out of it), on a personal level her steps traveled ever away from direct medical care. In her own words, Schumarry acknowledges that she is better at understanding and designing the business of medicine than at the actual one-on-one delivery of it though I bet she was, and would have remained, a very good emergency medicine physician. She astutely recognized where her talents were best suited and where she had unique advantages.

She has displayed marked stamina in her career choices. When one situation had more or less played out, such as implementing the Security Pacific National Bank health plan, she departed knowing that years of frustration would lie ahead. That decision entailed situation-awareness and self-confidence. She faced similar impasses at Aetna as medical director, and again at MedImpact, where her core values conflicted with the mission and cultures of these organizations and signaled to her that it was time to leave. When she departed, she did so with clear understanding of how these companies function within the overall delivery of health care. Not surprisingly, she left on good terms with management.

In addition to Schumarry's own intelligence in managing her professional journey, she has an invaluable ace in her pocket: she married a man who supported her choices. At most, only 50% of us managed this good judgment. She and her husband, Paul, have the kind of mutual trust and communication which give each the safety to make big decisions and to follow their independent careers.

Like many of our classmates, Schumarry's early life was rooted in the chaos of world history. She was born into wealth and privilege in 1946 near the Manchurian border in China. Her warlord grandfather managed by power and intrigue to rule his domain in the regional patchwork of conflicting alliances in the early years of the Republic of China and the subsequent Japanese occupation during World War II. Her parents married while her father was in medical school. He left China in 1948 for what was to be a two-year fellowship in surgery in the United States. Schumarry's mother, unwilling to leave the ease and comfort of her prosperous family, stayed behind in China with her young daughter. Though the political power of her grandfather protected the family, that shield dissolved after his death in late 1948 and the military victory of the Chinese communists over Northern China. Laden with as much wealth in the form of gold and jewelry as they could carry, Schumarry and her mother fled south to Beijing to live in her grandparents' summer home. But her warlord grandfather's history and her father's presence in the US condemned them in Mao's China. Schumarry was barred from entering school in Beijing. For this reason, more than anything else, Schumarry's mother decided they needed to leave, a difficult feat in the People's Republic of China. Fortunately the wife of China's Premier, Chou En Lai, a friend of Schumarry's mother, helped them escape to Hong Kong when Schumarry was ten. They relinquished all wealth and property with their departure, their life of ease now over.

Meanwhile, Schumarry's father dealt with the hurdles of obtaining a US medical license and a green card. He was working at the state hospital in Jamestown, North Dakota. In all the US, it would have been difficult to find a place more geographically and culturally distant from China but, in the context of the time, he was fortunate even to be there. The Chinese Exclusion Act of 1882, though officially repealed in 1943, erected nearly insurmountable barriers to immigration for another two decades.[6] Nonetheless, with the friendly help of the US immigration commissioner in North Dakota, twelve-year-old Schumarry and her mother were able to immigrate in 1957. Without that assistance, they would have been at the mercy of the quota system, a process that could have taken decades. Schumarry remembers arriving in North Dakota in the snow of midwinter

Schumarry Chao, 1971,
courtesy of Schumarry Chao

and speaking no English. The Chaos were the only non-Caucasian people in Jamestown. They faced the friendly, but interminable, inquiry: "How do you like it here?" Schumarry remembers liking the charm of the small town.

Schumarry's father obtained his license to practice medicine in California when she was thirteen. They soon traded snow and charm for Southern California. Academically good in math and science, Schumarry managed to catch up in English and skip a grade. She attended high school in Redondo Beach. Those years were a time of family turmoil with a move to a new home, the birth of a baby sister, and little money as her father set up his plastic surgery practice. Schumarry worked after-school jobs as a waitress and, like Faith Fitzgerald, as ticket seller at movie theaters. Throughout her childhood, her parents always emphasized education and diligence as the road to self-sufficiency and financial stability.

Schumarry stayed close to her family in college and continued to work to offset the cost. She attended the University of Southern California, and, though she lived on campus in the school dormitories, she returned home most weekends to help with household chores. Focused on getting good grades in order to apply to medical school, an aspiration endorsed by her father, Schumarry continued to be academically competitive in math and science, though college-level English courses remained difficult. "College was not particularly fun," Schumarry reported, until it soared senior year. She was crowned "Miss Chinatown" for Los Angeles—finally a fun year before medical school.

Initially medical school at UCSF was a lesson in survival skills. It was the first time Schumarry really lived away from home. She termed the first two years as "intense and overwhelming" and saw herself as an "outsider." She recalled instances of inappropriate treatment because she was female. For example, in the first year in gross anatomy, she shared a female cadaver with three male classmates. One night the boys added a penis to the cadaver's pelvic anatomy. The next morning, they waited like a row of crows on a fence to witness Schumarry's reaction as she removed the sheet from the body. "Did one of you boys leave something behind last night?" she asked. Her survival skills sharpened quickly. Later she was penalized by a poor grade in her neurology rotation after she refused to date the supervising neurology resident. Sadness added to her difficulty after the death of her good friend and our classmate, Bernardo, in a vehicle crash in Guatemala. Nonetheless she did well overall in the clinical years, especially in her surgical rotations. In fact, the formidable Dr. F. William Blaisdell, Chief of Surgery at San Francisco General Hospital, encouraged her to consider a surgical residency.

During a fourth-year externship in Hawaii, Schumarry met her future husband, Paul Tsou, an orthopedic surgery resident several years ahead of her at UCSF, also doing a rotation in Honolulu. After four dates in ten days, he proposed. They married a few months later upon return to California. Now, nearly fifty years later, Schumarry counts this decision as the best one of her life.

In 1971, armed with her medical degree and, importantly, with the support of her husband, Schumarry began her remarkable and unusual career trajectory which she could not have foreseen—or even imagined. No woman in the study had a career remotely comparable. Indeed, for the era, perhaps no other physician in the country pursued a similar path. Like an elliptical staircase winding ever upward, adding layer upon layer, her career advanced until the top floor afforded a view of the entire landscape below. While Bonnie changed careers by a giant leap without a parachute, Schumarry built her edifice layer upon logical layer, conquering each element of the structure as she ascended.

That Schumarry would take this journey was not obvious at the beginning. She started slowly. After a surgical internship at Highland Hospital East Bay in Oakland, she took the next year off in Hong Kong where her husband had a fellowship in orthopedic surgery. But after that, her career honeymoon ended. They returned to Los Angeles to please Schumarry's parents at "their insistence," she said. Schumarry began an otolaryngology residency in the Los Angeles County Hospital-University of Southern California (USC) program. Halfway through the second year, though, she reluctantly quit the program due to the poor health of her newborn daughter, unable to handle the heavy call schedule with a sick child. Instead she accepted a job at the LA County Hospital to head the trauma services in the emergency department, a position for which her three and a half years of surgical training made her eminently qualified. Looking back, this was it—the first big step up the staircase.

For the next twelve years, until 1987, Schumarry worked in emergency medicine. When the American Board of Medical Specialties voted in

1979 to recognize emergency medicine as a separate medical specialty, Schumarry was in the inaugural group to become board-certified. As the physician managing the LA County Hospital/USC service, Schumarry had responsibility for writing protocols and designing drills for every type of emergency or disaster situation that might arise in Southern California. Earthquakes, floods, fires, epidemics, out of control rock concerts—any mass casualty event that might occur fell under her purview. This experience placed her at the leading edge of understanding how health delivery systems work. After Los Angeles was selected to host the 1984 Olympics, she became involved in the early preparation of protocols for the pre-Olympic events and, subsequently, for the Olympics. The inadequate medical response to an athlete's severe injury from a diving accident in pre-Olympic tryouts the year before in Canada led to keen awareness by the US Olympic Committee of the need for careful planning for any mishap in the athletic events in Los Angeles.

In 1983, Schumarry became *el jefe*—the Chief Medical Officer for Olympic Villages for the 1984 Summer Olympics. This was huge. It was an honor and an endorsement of her abilities, and, in her view, "a once-in-a-lifetime opportunity." It had been five decades since the US had last hosted the summer Olympics, coincidentally also in Los Angeles. The complexity of the event had grown exponentially. Reagan was president, the Cold War reigned, the Soviets boycotted the Games in retaliation for the US boycott of the 1980 Moscow Olympics, and China returned after three decades. The massive security efforts by local, state, and federal agencies on behalf of the Olympics left the LA police militarized in a way that lasted long after the Games ended.[7] Into this complicated and manifold effort, Schumarry entered. Undaunted. As head of the delivery systems for medical emergencies and trauma, her responsibilities included writing all of the relevant protocols and overseeing their implementation. The planning alone took a year. She had to grapple with the logistics, finances, and politics surrounding the delivery of medical care in a multicultural milieu. There were thousands of details. The medical services required coordination with insurance systems, fire and police departments, armies of volunteers, and the media. And everything had to be inserted into crowded and diverse Los Angeles over fifteen days as the city welcomed 3.5 million attendees.

The Olympic games proceeded smoothly. The medical services ran flawlessly. Schumarry deserved a gold medal.

After the Olympics, Schumarry returned to USC. Armed with her organizational prowess, she approached the USC administration with the suggestion that she set up an insurance health plan for the school's students and faculty. At this point, Schumarry's career diverged from direct patient care to strategies of patient care. Arguably the initial steps began years before in organizing the emergency medical services first for the LA County Hospital and then for the LA Olympics. But this decision marked the fork in her road away from direct medical care to management.

The plan Schumarry conceived for USC would create a network such that all patient referrals would go back to the medical school. The cost of the system would therefore stay within the institution. The system additionally could be leveraged to encourage referrals from other providers in LA. The USC administration recognized the appeal of such a system, especially in terms of the cost savings, and gave a provisional endorsement if the new system could be organized against a six-week fiscal deadline that the university faced. Compressed within this extraordinarily short time frame, Schumarry managed the negotiations for a USC Healthcare Plan/ Insurance structure that included agreements with hospitals, physician groups, pharmacies, employees, and a myriad of other entities. Though there were problems in the initial rollout of the system, she defined and implemented the basic framework of the system in record time. Over the next few years, the insurance plan underwent many refinements and proved to be very successful. Additionally, to enhance her business training,

Schumarry completed USC's two-year Executive Master of Business Administration program while working at the health plan full-time. She graduated valedictorian of her MBA class, no surprise to anyone who knew her.

But remember, the time was the 1980s. Ronald Reagan was president. Liberalism fell from fashion. Schumarry had existed in a nearly all-male world throughout her career—from surgery resident to USC Director of Emergency Trauma to Medical Director for the Olympic Villages to architect and head of the USC Health Plan. And she was a pleasant, petite, and pretty Asian female. She stood out. She was unusual. Men noticed. Inappropriate events occurred. Schumarry was basically alone to cope with the quicksand.

Early in her career in the LA County Hospital, part of the overall evaluation process included opinions of the faculty by the residents. Two male residents propositioned her by offering her good evaluations if she would sleep with them. She refused and reported them to her male supervisor. He cavalierly responded, "Boys will be boys." Other senior people recommended that Schumarry bring legal action against the system for not supporting her. In the end, Schumarry followed the advice of one trusted friend who counseled that she had a very bright career ahead of her and, if she brought legal action, the episode would forever follow her and be linked to her reputation. She also realized that legal action would entangle her in a negative experience at a time when she wanted to move forward on a positive path. This experience led Schumarry ultimately to resign her LA County/USC appointment. It marked the right time to move on.

Risks lurked from many sides for a professional woman. Schumarry developed remarkable savvy in her ability to read the signals of danger and nuances of problems—and to deal with them. In the many negotiations she faced as she progressively entered the business side of health care, she tried never to back an opponent into a corner. She sought always to retain a face-saving route of exit for her adversary or for herself if needed. Her ability to get along with others, professionals and nonprofessionals alike, perhaps dating from her many childhood transitions from China to Hong Kong to North Dakota to Los Angeles and her feeling of being an outsider, helped her in both the medical and business worlds. In our conversation, Schumarry added with a smile, she feels some of her success in business resides in "my advantage in being able to assess situations while others had their guards down by underestimating me as a female and Asian."

Schumarry understood how to organize her life as a professional working full-time and as a wife and mother. Throughout her career, she had live-in housekeepers to help with the children and manage the household work. Lillian identified the physicians, like Schumarry, within the study as having "good executive function." I know what she meant by that terminology. In my own life working full-time and raising two children, I often felt I was additionally running a small business juggling childcare help, house cleaners, and gardeners.

By 1988 the USC Health Plan under Schumarry's leadership was running well and saving the institution considerable money in providing health care for students and employees. Proposing and successfully implementing this plan had been an audacious move by Schumarry, and the administration at USC rightly deserved credit in its support of her. The plan's success did not go unnoticed by the Board of Trustees of USC. In particular, Robert H. Smith, President and CEO of Security Pacific National Bank (SPNB), USC graduate and USC Trustee, took note. He was impressed.

Security Pacific was a large and complex bank. Like sprawl and smog, the bank grew with Los Angeles from mergers with smaller banks predominantly in southern California but also in the western United States and Pacific Rim countries. When Smith became SPNB's young and innovative president in 1987, he appropriately focused on the bank's financial profitability. Health care costs for its 10,000 employees did not escape his attention. He contacted Schumarry in 1988 and asked her to set up a health care plan for employees in the bank's 600 domestic branches. In her acceptance of this challenge, Schumarry pivoted to become a businesswoman, albeit one with a profound understanding of medicine. Smith was a businessman with a profound understanding of banking. They could communicate.

Though Smith hired Schumarry to design and implement a health plan, he far from ceded control. Her success had to fit within certain hard-headed management parameters for the proposed $186,000,000 bank healthcare system. He listed the outcomes he expected like battle orders. Schumarry's directive was to reduce the annual healthcare cost increase by well over 50%, to incur no lawsuits, and to develop the plan in such a way that no unions resulted.

Schumarry took the assignment even though she knew it would be difficult and risky. But she was buoyed by the knowledge that she had the full support of the bank president and top management.

If Smith demonstrated a hard-headed attitude, Schumarry equaled him as she set to work. Her basic concept in dealing with insurance companies was "shared-risk." If an insurance company could increase its profit by having the Security Pacific's account, then it would have to agree to cap the risk of cost overruns to the bank's health plan. The bank had previously used Aetna as the administrator for their healthcare plan. When Schumarry suggested they assume some of the risk for cost increases, Aetna refused. So Schumarry fired Aetna—almost like a missile vaporizing a target. She then worked out a highly satisfactory shared-risk arrangement with Blue Cross of California.

An important part of Schumarry's mandate from Smith was to avoid lawsuits and the formation of unions based on health plan issues. To do this, she switched sides. She led focus groups of employees to learn what they wanted in a health plan and how they defined quality. The results astonished her. The top ten items had nothing to do with physicians or the quality of health care. Instead, employee priorities prominently included comfort of waiting rooms, length of wait times, quality of magazines in waiting rooms, and other unsuspected parameters which she would not have guessed from her prior career. As a result of her experience with focus groups and working with the bank's managers, Schumarry gained an entirely new perspective in how patients thought and how the consumer, both patient and corporation, viewed health care. She credited these insights to be her greatest lessons in understanding healthcare delivery.

By 1990, Schumarry had 200 employees working on the health plan under her at the bank. While they were in the early stages of the plan's implementation, Security Pacific began negotiations for merger with Bank of America. One cannot overestimate the size, complexity, and "frantic chaos surrounding the deal" in combining two giant banks with the sure knowledge that the merger would result in duplicate departments and inevitable layoffs. Insecurity about their future with the bank beset the employees under Schumarry. She read the tea leaves. In the turmoil of the near-term, an innovative approach to health care would be a casualty. After securing some protections for her staff, Schumarry left the bank in 1991.

Meanwhile insurance companies no doubt took note of the huge employee pool that would result from the merger of the two banks. And Aetna undoubtedly had not forgotten that Schumarry had fired them from the Security Pacific account several years earlier. So Aetna did what Abraham Lincoln would have done. Hire your rival. Aetna recruited Schumarry to become their Medical Director.

Ready for another challenge, Schumarry accepted. The prospect of learning health care from "inside the tent" of a large insurance company was attractive. At USC and Security Pacific, she had always negotiated contracts from the outside. Her family was supportive. Schumarry moved to Hartford, her son transferred to Phillips Andover Academy, her daughter matriculated at Stanford, her husband stayed in LA, and the airlines gained a new frequent flyer. Schumarry found Aetna, and the East Coast in general, to be very different cultures from the West Coast. For one thing, there were fewer Asians. She adapted, however, and developed many friendships.

The Aetna years were a wild time. Bill Clinton had won the presidential election, Zoe Baird, recently derailed from becoming Attorney General by the Nannygate fracas (when it was discovered she employed illegal immigrants and moreover failed to pay Social Security taxes for them), was general counsel of Aetna, and the White House wanted healthcare reform. Schumarry became the official medical spokesperson for Aetna on reform to the government and media. Previously, the Aetna Medical Director functioned primarily in risk management. Schumarry's new role was unanticipated. Overnight she became a media star.

Because of the new high visibility of her position, Schumarry was asked to attend Aetna Board meetings, an invitation not previously extended to the Medical Director. There she heard frequent reference to ROSHE. Conversations often would devolve into speculation about how some decision would affect ROSHE or how a department contributed to ROSHE. Schumarry asked its meaning. ROSHE turned out to be Aetna's gold standard, "return on shareholder equity," its corporate Kool-Aid and North Star.

All in all, at Aetna Schumarry gained valuable insight in understanding corporate politics and entrenched, ingrained cultures. Meetings generated meetings which in turn generated more meetings. Little got done. Loyalty was nonexistent. Corporate culture affirmed, "If you want loyalty, get a dog." Although Schumarry learned a great deal at Aetna, she recognized that it was time to leave. After two fast-paced and interesting years, she departed on good terms with the company, waved *adios*, and caught the next flight west.

Schumarry returned to Los Angeles. In addition to maintaining her medical license and continuing education credits throughout her moves from USC Health Plan director to medical director of Security Pacific, she had kept her emergency medicine skills current by working shifts in emergency departments approximately once a week. It was only in Hartford with Aetna that she became too busy to commit to a specific shift rotation. Once back in LA, she considered resuming her career in hands-on emergency medicine.

However, USC offered other options. The USC Health Plan that she had started years before remained up and running well. The administration suggested that she work for them in evaluation of risk of capitation (accepting a fixed payment arrangement as health service providers). The evaluation would entail the assessment of the financial risk that the University would assume from Medical School capitation contracts with outside insurers and the determination of the premium of the University health plan for employees and students. She accepted and once again became an employee of USC on a part-time basis for the next two years. Additionally she engaged in consultive work on strategic development for various healthcare groups outside of USC. Independent entrepreneurship entered her repertoire.

While Schumarry was winding down her work for USC, by chance she met Frederick Howe, the pharmacist-founder of a company based in San Diego called MedImpact Pharmacy. The company was in the early start-up phase in 1995. Schumarry and Howe had a conversation. Howe then offered Schumarry the position of Chief Medical Officer and Senior Vice President of Strategic Development. She thus joined MedImpact Pharmacy as the only physician in an organization dominated by pharmacists. The company was a pharmacy benefit management (PBM) organization, then a little-known, intermediary type of structure that straddled the abyss between drugs and patients. During Schumarry's seven and a half years at MedImpact, the company grew from fourteen to 200 employees and from 200,000 to twenty-eight million pharmacy benefit members. She set up a management structure in the early phase of the company's growth and learned the pharmacy business, especially *how the money flows.*

In brief, PBMs began in the late 1960s as intermediary organizations among pharmaceutical companies that manufacture drugs, healthcare providers that prescribe drugs, and insurance organizations that pay for drugs. By the 1970s and 1980s, PBMs had become major players in health care. They were initially important in steering providers to lower cost drugs, especially to generic drugs. However, the financial profit of a PBM is built on processing fees and spreads/rebates in the drug supply chain. A few large consolidated PBMs like MedImpact came to dominate the marketplace. Beginning around 2002, the PBM system quietly began to move into marketing more expensive, brand-named drugs. More and more, the profits of the companies came from the back-end negotiated agreements with drug manufacturers and retail companies and not from processing fees.

Where the money flowed in the industry became increasingly obvious. By 2003, the evolving issues of this type of business model disturbed Schumarry. She had faced a similar dilemma in her tenure at Aetna. In both cases, she recognized that she could neither change the business models of the companies nor embrace them. In 2003, she left MedImpact.

Schumarry knew herself well. She also had a bedrock understanding of the importance of recognizing what you can change and what you cannot change in any given organization.

Schumarry returned to consulting which she continues to the present. She founded an independent consulting company, SHC & Associates, that specializes in healthcare solutions for pragmatic strategic planning and implementation for all elements of health care—consumers, providers, employers, insurers, and PBMs. Schumarry leveraged her unique relationships with various experts in 2007 to establish an advisory council of sixty key thought-leaders and decision-makers to provide business insights and timely feedback on strategies and tactics. This Peer-to-Peer Market

Advisory Council is a group of trusted and confidential colleagues with whom Schumarry discusses ideas and opinions for the benefit of her clients. Among her current activities, she leads policy groups for Medicare and Medicaid and for China on healthcare economics. She performs evaluations on various healthcare plans and advises pharmaceutical companies on drug-to-market strategies. Additionally she is in demand as a moderator on panel discussions and meetings involving healthcare issues and pharmaceuticals and regularly gives lectures to physicians to help them better understand the business of health care. As she explained to me, "I have done many lectures for Kaiser and the USC Master of Medical Management program. I find that most physicians have little understanding of the business of health care, its impact on their practice, and how to anticipate or position themselves for market changes. This has become a passion of mine."

As one of the few physicians who has been directly involved since the beginning of healthcare management, she possesses a unique perspective. She entered the field before it was defined and well before it was a career that a physician would consider. For her, one successful step led to the next as she established a track record, forever upward on corporate ladders. In the end, she is one of the few physicians today who has had hands-on leadership and management positions in direct patient care, payer management, insurance companies, and pharmacy benefit management. In all these areas she has been held accountable for the decisions she made and the outcomes of those decisions. As a result, she has acquired a profound understanding of the connections between medicine and business as a single complex picture—among government policy, providers, insurers, pharmacy and device companies. If one sector is changed, then that causes changes in other sectors.

Schumarry gives examples. With the enactment of pharmacy benefits for seniors (Medicare Part D), generics increased from 45% to 70% because of the incentives put in place to use generics. The Affordable Care Act

Schumarry Chao and her husband, recent photo, courtesy of Schumarry Chao

brought sunlight between physicians and drug and device companies that resulted in more direct-to-consumer policies. The increase in medical-legal cases against some surgeons educated the public and government about the relationships with the makers of devices and their users. The electronic medical record was, in part, designed to increase revenue by automatically including as billable items procedures, such as parts of the physical exam like pelvic or rectal exams, that physicians may or may not have performed.

In looking back over her career, Schumarry credits her turning point to be a moment of self-recognition of her strengths. At some point after the LA Olympics, she realized that she was, in her words, an "average physician," but she was much better than others in terms of her creative ideas in how to structure and organize systems within medicine. The business side of health care formed her "groove and calling."

Bonnie's spirituality defined her from her earliest memories. She found a refuge in the Catholic convent schools she attended where certain nuns recognized not only her intellect but her empathetic, nonjudgmental nature. Her spirituality manifested not as specifically Catholic but as an ability to pluck from the universe signals that resonated with her generosity and desire to help others. Many people, and I include myself, fail to be quiet or receptive enough even to be aware that guidance in life can come in this way. Fortunately for Bonnie, she learned as a child that she could hear this hum of the universe. Not that it was all-protective. She made mistakes like many of us, most notably in marriage. But her ability to call on her inner resources to find her way remained her guidepost. In the end, it gave her the courage to step into the unknown and define a new form of healing.

Whereas Bonnie expressed her sources of courage in spiritual language, Schumarry used more conventional language of "listening to her gut" as she progressively made one career change after another, stepwise, away from traditional medical practice to the business of medicine. One could envision lists of pros and cons. A scientific process. And highly efficient and logical, the way a person grounded in science and mathematics would approach a decision. I can relate. My model would have been similar. Yet the courage to make these decisions should not be underestimated. Each change embraced unknown territory where virtually no physician before had treaded, certainly no female and especially no Asian female physician. The territories were male and dominated by financial parameters independent of moral or ethical considerations.

Within this study, Bonnie and Schumarry represent the two physicians who most radically changed their practices. The ability of Schumarry to excel in each of her positions within the business world was enhanced because she is a physician, even though her positions did not require a medical degree. Her view from the bridge remained unique. Bonnie's long and intensive submersion as a pediatric oncologist gave her the foundation to know how to use her talents to their highest purpose. Her ability to counsel rested on the sum of her entire life experience.

CHAPTER 6

LINEAR CAREERS AND COMPLICATED LIVES

In October of 2016, I flew to Santa Rosa to interview Dr. Nancy Doyle. Though we had stayed in touch over the years, especially through our UCSF class reunions, this was my first visit to her home and community. It was well-timed. Within a year, the worst wildfire in the history of California devastated Santa Rosa. And, as I was to learn, the unfortunate health problems that beset Nancy's daughter would escalate as much as the flames.

Looking back, I had viewed our lives as similar. We each entered specialties in medicine that we loved and then, straight as arrows, practiced those specialties for the next thirty years. We each had a son, then a daughter, and loved being a mother. And during the turmoil of the Vietnam War, we each married a man on the eve of his induction into the Army who ultimately presented us with personal challenges.

Nevertheless, decade after decade, we both managed.

To a significant degree, I think our professions were our anchors. My confidence in myself grew from my competence as a physician. Indeed, my profession became my sanctuary from which I derived strength to tackle nonprofessional problems. Like Faith at UC Davis, Nancy became a pre-eminent physician in her Santa Rosa community, widely recognized as the referral pediatrician who could solve complex problems, and with her experience came self-assurance. She clearly had the fortitude to surmount situations that would seem impossible to most people.

Lillian might have predicted Nancy's professional strengths. On the California Personality Inventory test we took upon entrance to medical school, Nancy scored the highest of the entire group of fifty-eight women in Responsibility, a measurement of reasonableness and concern with duties and obligations. What was unusual was that Nancy also had a very high score on Achievement via Independence, a measurement of intellectual independence and intellectual capability and efficiency. As a psychologist, Lillian noted that these attributes were rarely coupled in a single individual—and proved very powerful when found together. Her psychological interpretation of Nancy's tests in 1967 was that the profile indicated a physician who would demonstrate creativity and independence in solving problems and would remain on task until the problem was solved. Without question, Nancy's career demonstrated these strengths.

In contrast, my psychological profile on entrance to medical school had no distinguishing characteristics within the overall cohort of women. My choice of pathology did fit my intellect and interest very well and allowed me to become quite proficient in the specialty. As a result, by mid-career, I felt secure as a respected member of Virginia Mason Medical Center. Without question, this provided me with the confidence and courage to face the eventual difficulties in my marriage and find solutions.

Responsibility And Perseverance

It's hard to remember now, but large portions of the United States were rural in the first decades of the twentieth century. Large families scraped out livings on small farms. Educational opportunities were limited. Nancy's parents both came from such backgrounds.

Her father was born in 1918 on Montana land homesteaded by his parents where they eked out a hard life as farmers and raised their twelve children. Nancy's father had his first job as the "bus driver" for his rural school as an eight-year-old. He picked up other farm children in a horse-drawn wagon, and together they rode to school. He fed his horse as he ate his own lunch over the noon hour. With no possibility of education beyond high school, he joined the US Army. His natural talents in machinery and engineering found good use in airplane maintenance in the Army Air Corps.

By December of 1941, this responsible young man had advanced to be flight chief of the Army Air Corps 73rd Fighter-Pursuit Squadron where he supervised all aircraft maintenance at Wheeler Army Airfield near Honolulu. On Sunday, December 7th, at 7:55 am, he awoke to sirens and jumped from bed, pausing only long enough to pull on his slacks. His buddies, running out of the barracks slightly before him, became the first casualties killed in the initial wave of Japanese dive bombers bent on destroying fighter planes on the ground before attacking battleships in Honolulu Harbor. That morning, only one Army plane survived to fight back, though by salvaging usable parts, the Wheeler ground crew had three or four more in the air by evening. "There was no fear until afterward," Nancy's father said of the bombing.[1] "You just go about your business and do what you have to do. Later, after you have time to think about what happened...Oh, boy." For the luck of a few seconds' pause, Nancy's father survived.

Within six months of the Pearl Harbor attack, on June 7th, her father landed on Midway Atoll with the US Navy the day after Japanese Admiral Yamamoto ordered his crippled fleet to retreat and end the Battle of Midway. On their first day, he and his fellow soldiers had the sad duty to bury over 300 of the American forces killed during the initial days of the battle, casualties from the Japanese bombardment of military ground installations. They remained stationed on Midway for a year in order to repair and extend the vital airfields and defensive structures. The two islands and surrounding coral reef that composed Midway Atoll, first reported and claimed by the United States in 1859, proved invaluable for the remainder of the war. Eventually, and during the lifetime of Nancy's father, Midway graduated to a nonmilitary future as a site reserved for nesting seabirds, the Midway Atoll National Wildlife Refuge and Battle of Midway National Memorial.[2]

Many years later, Nancy recorded her interview with her father about Pearl Harbor and Midway. His experience is now part of the Library of Congress record of World War II.

Nancy's father stayed in the military for his entire career, rising to the rank of chief master sergeant in the US Air Force, the successor to the Army Air Corps, the highest rank possible for a service member without a college degree. He always regretted his lack of higher education and remained an autodidact throughout his life. He read extensively, took college-level night classes whenever possible, and eventually accumulated enough credits to earn a degree from the University of Nebraska when he was sixty. As he progressed through his military career, he mentored younger men and, in an ideal world, would have liked to be a teacher and counselor.

Nancy's parents met and married during the war when her father was stationed in Washington, DC. The background of Nancy's mother was not unlike that of her father.

Nancy's maternal grandfather worked hard and succeeded as a farmer in rural Virginia. He also served as the local sheriff. His wife worked equally hard as a farm wife doing all the chores, including caring for the farm animals and cooking for the ranch hands as well as her family. But, in Nancy's description of her grandmother's life, what stood out most vividly was her career as a teacher. As a sixteen-year-old girl, she lied about her age in order to gain admittance into a one-year teachers' college. Once married and living on their farm, she started a one-room school on their land and taught there for over thirty years—in addition to all of her farm chores.

Nancy's mother did well academically and would have liked to go to college, but, given the times and circumstances, "college was not for girls," according to Nancy's grandfather. Instead, she became a secretary and proved to be an invaluable assistant to a senator for whom she worked in

Washington, DC, and for generals later when the family was stationed in Alaska and beyond.

Of her mother, Nancy said, "She never complained or said an unkind word. She accepted challenges and hardships with quiet reserve and always found a way to make things work." Nancy credited her mother as the steady glue that held the family together. Throughout Nancy's life, her mother, and the memory of her grandmother, served as role models and inspirations of strength. To the present day, it is to her mother's example of love and perseverance that Nancy ascribes her ability to handle the major problems that she now faces.

Nancy recounted the story of her childhood through the military bases where she and her parents lived, her personal version of *The Canterbury Tales.* She and her parents formed a "unit of three," in Nancy's words. As long as they were together, it didn't matter where on earth they were, they were okay.

Nancy was born in 1945 at Andrews Air Force Base in Maryland. Her mother, sick with pneumonia during delivery, held Nancy for two minutes before she was sequestered for treatment, away from even viewing her baby daughter for two weeks. Nancy's twenty-six-year-old father brought his daughter home and exclusively cared for her. After all, he was a farm boy. He knew how to handle problems. In the first week, Nancy threw up constantly until her allergy to cow's milk was determined. Nancy thinks that her closeness with her father was imprinted on both of them during those first difficult weeks of her life.

After Andrews, Warren Air Force Base in Cheyenne, Wyoming, was home during the Korean War and Nancy's preschool years. They had a brief stay at Selfridge Air Force Base near Detroit, where they lived in base housing and where everyone was supposedly the same. But when Nancy was six, she discovered everyone was not the same. Her new friend, a Black girl in her class, could not come to her home to play. It was a precautionary decision by both her mother and her friend's mother—and a sad comment on the times confusing to the six-year-olds. Next they moved to Kansas where they lived in a house for the first time, "like normal people," she said. Her father taught ROTC at Kansas State College (now Kansas State University) in Manhattan from 1952 to1956.

And so Nancy narrated her life, move by move, usually at two-year intervals. She developed rituals to make peace with each move. Nancy would sit on top of packed and stacked boxes and announce "farewell." Then off they went. At each new base, Nancy tried to adopt everyone as family. She said it would take a year to make a close friend, and she always tried—before she mounted the stacked boxes again.

What plagued Nancy as a child was neither the moves nor the scramble to make new friends. It was asthma. Was her early cow's milk allergy a clue? Beginning at age two, she suffered frequent attacks. At the time, there was no medical treatment for asthma. She remembers attacks that would last for three to five days. She would sit on a chair facing the back with her arms elevated and hanging over the backrest as she struggled to breathe, often hallucinating. "My poor mother sitting up with me all those nights," she said. As she became older, the asthma worsened. And, to this day, asthma and the pulmonary sequelae remain Nancy's most significant health problem.

After Kansas living "like normal people," the family departed for the Territory of Alaska in 1956. As they drove to Fairbanks, Nancy had a particularly severe attack of asthma. For the first time, she was treated with prednisone by a country doctor in Montana. She said that it was "almost life changing to finally get an effective treatment. My attack broke within a day."

As Nancy told me this, it sounded like an omen. Her world also broke open in Alaska. They lived in Fairbanks for two and a half years and celebrated with the Indigenous Alaskans when the Territory became a state in January of 1959.

Nancy's school there was excellent and marked the beginning of her love of science. In the seventh grade, her health teacher taught the subject through the physiology of the human body, explaining the metabolic processes behind health and development. Nancy loved it. She found the inner workings of the human body the most interesting subject she had studied.

Nancy and her best friend, an Indigenous girl who lived in an orphanage, academically led their classes and received all the prizes. The air base featured a teen club with swimming, dances, target shooting, bowling, and, for Nancy, her first boyfriend. Best of all, her health was good with few asthma attacks in the clean air of the far north.

Nancy's father promised her that they would stay in one place for her high school experience. Fortunately the years of 1959 through 1963 were a time of relative peace. He could keep his promise. The family bid their farewell to the new State of Alaska in 1959 and drove to Lake Charles, Louisiana. There, Nancy attended the St. Charles Academy, a Catholic high school for girls. She became a star. She sang in the choir, played sports, and excelled in academics. As a senior, she edited the yearbook, captured the chemistry award, won gold medals in French and biology for the State of Louisiana, and was elected "school sweetheart." She graduated as valedictorian. Her father had kept his promise. But the day she graduated, they left Louisiana for good.

A pivotal encounter occurred at the St. Charles Academy. In Nancy's biology class, a young substitute teacher taught for two months as she awaited her own entrance to medical school. She became a mentor and encouraged Nancy's aspiration to become a doctor, thoughts Nancy had harbored since seventh grade in her health class in Alaska. Nancy also loved the television program, *Dr. Kildare*. But her own experiences with doctors in her numerous attacks of asthma had not been good. Neither

were her father's. Complications from hernia surgery after Nancy's birth
had rendered him sterile. Her parents often referred to the bad outcome of
the surgery when they discussed their disappointment of not being able to
have more children.

Yet fundamentally, despite overwhelming evidence to the contrary,
Nancy thought she was not smart enough to become a doctor. She had
concepts of herself that were in conflict.

Throughout her childhood as she transferred from school to school, in
each new situation, she had to hide her intelligence in order to be accepted.
The cardinal rule was not to stand out. "Never let the other kids know you're
smart. No one likes the smarty ones," she told herself. During the year it took
to make friends, she had to lie low. In addition, she had an idealized picture
in her mind of what a doctor was and how much he knew. She didn't know
any doctors with whom to compare herself. And throughout her life, she
had the view that she had to figure out things for herself. You never ask for
help—you just do it—an ideal of self-sufficiency that grew from her military
background and her parents' example. In her psyche, none of this added up
to being a physician. This mindset followed Nancy to college.

She entered Ohio State University in Columbus in 1963, the "unit of
three" if not living together, still close to each other, her parents at nearby
Lockbourne Air Force Base. Awakened in Alaska, her love of science
flourished at Ohio State while the thought of medical school quietly lurked
in the background. As she entered the university, she studied the curriculum
under the premed heading and signed up for every required course. If
nothing else, the subjects sounded interesting. Nancy majored in anatomy.
In her science courses, her classmates were mostly males. One in particular,
a rude and cruel football player, sat next to her in anatomy. One day he
mentioned that he was premed. That did it. She said to herself, "If someone
as nasty and mean as he can become a doctor, then I surely can." Self-doubt
began to vaporize. She doubled down on courses and added German and

organic chemistry for premed —"just in case I do apply and need them. It was always there. I just didn't know how I would get there—until finally it's time, I'm going," she remembered thinking. She visited the premed advisor, a woman who, looking up with a smile, said, "Where have you been? I've been waiting for you."

Discouraging remarks ceased to matter. In college, she dated a medical student at Ohio State, one of her discouragers, and went to some classes with him. A female med-student friend of his, staring at Nancy, said, "You look like Miss America. You'll never make it in med school." When Nancy had an untoward reaction to a vaccination, the flight surgeon at Lockbourne that she saw advised her against medicine, saying, "You're a woman. It's too hard." Ironically four years later when he was a new faculty member at UCSF, Nancy saw him and, with a laugh, said, "Your advice didn't work." Nancy applied to three medical schools, received admittance to each, and chose UCSF based on visions of California lifestyle of sun and beaches.

Medicine fit Nancy's intellect and interests. Equally well, it also fit her moral views on life. Religion played an important role in her family. Both parents were devout and centered their lives on the fundamental principles of the Golden Rule and Christian morality. Although Nancy's Methodist mother did not go to church, Nancy and her father attended Catholic services every Sunday and were confirmed together when Nancy was in the fourth grade. While she discounted much of the doctrine, such as rejecting any thought that her wonderful mother would go to Hell because she was Methodist, Nancy accepted Catholicism in a universalist way. She described her father as deeply religious and spiritual. "He practiced his faith to his last breath," she told me. Whereas she rejected Catholicism *per se*, the Christian calling to help the infirm and ease suffering remain fundamental to Nancy's concept of her life and practice of medicine.

The first two years at UCSF were tough. Nancy's relatively sequestered military life gave way to the no-holds-barred life of San Francisco in the turmoil of the late '60s. Life on Mount Parnassus swirled amid the Haight-Ashbury drug and hippie scene, anti-war demonstrations, and the civil rights movement. The order and respect for hierarchy that had been fundamental to her life were absent. She witnessed a type of rudeness and disrespect for our professors that she had never previously encountered—with fellow students walking out of lectures they thought boring or irrelevant, for example.

Moreover, her budget was tight. She shared an apartment with two women, sleeping on an air mattress on the floor, and was often hungry. Though she liked her roommates, they presented complications. The stoned brother of one roommate would move in with equally stoned friends for days at a time and consume their entire food supply. The order of her life basically disappeared.

Honed throughout her childhood, Nancy's ability to adopt a group of friends as family gradually reasserted itself. She and three male classmates banded together with ties that last to this day. With them, she questioned everything, from her Catholicism, to the war in Vietnam, to her role in medicine.

One painful memory lives on, unabated. A male classmate damned her father as a murderer to her because he was in the military. It was overwhelming to Nancy—damn anyone but not her father whom she loved and respected beyond measure. Having lived through those angry days myself, I remember how it was. Anyone in uniform was vilified—including drafted doctors. My then boyfriend, as a captain in the Army medical corps, was spat on in the San Francisco airport as he returned from Korea in uniform on a mission of mercy bringing a Korean orphan to the US for heart surgery. And the political assassinations kept mounting, year after year. As I marched against the war, I drew ever closer to being part of it. It was a schizophrenic time for even the most grounded of people. Nonetheless, to blame Nancy's father for the war in Vietnam was vile ignorance.

In our third year, we began our clinical rotations. As students, we would be added to a team consisting of an intern, a resident, and an attending faculty physician. It was the classic apprenticeship model, involving a bit of hands-on work and a lot of observing and listening. For the student, much of the teaching came from the intern and resident. For Nancy, her first medical experience set the standard for her career. Faith Fitzgerald was her intern. Nancy won the lottery. She remembered watching Faith talk to a patient about treatment while she passed the patient her lunch tray and poured her milk. Faith's clear message emphasized that the patient was a person first, worthy of respect, and, in Faith's words, "common acts of humanity." This example translated into permission for Nancy always to act as herself, always to be the open, caring, sensitive, empathetic person she was and never to adopt the remote, authoritarian persona she observed in some physicians. Empathy combined with knowledge became her north star, not her white coat.

One of Nancy's clinical rotations during her fourth year took her to the pediatric service at San Francisco General Hospital under the leadership of Dr. Mel Grossman. From the first day, Nancy loved the resilience and toughness of her young patients, most of whom came from difficult circumstances, including poverty, drug addiction, and violence in the home. In pediatrics, she found her mission within medicine.

Until the last few weeks of medical school, few of us were aware of the UCSF Gold Headed Cane Society. Such an odd name for a society within medicine. Even Skull and Bones sounded more appropriate. Still, the Society was an important tradition and remarkably apt for our era. Each year the UCSF Gold Headed Cane Society awarded membership to the three physicians in the graduating class who exemplified the best qualities of a true physician. Of the three, one received an actual cane topped in 14 karat gold. Who would have guessed that our class would change the school's history over a cane draped in gold?

The Gold Headed Cane Society

When our forefathers, a group that included four physicians, signed the Declaration of Independence in 1776, not every tradition in King George III's realm was forsaken. The respected image of the physician remained intact in America, more deservedly so after the Flexner Report of 1910 led to marked improvement in the standards of medical education in the US.[3] Yet a few royal relics lived on unchanged. The gold-headed cane is one.

In the England of the 17th to the 19th centuries, a cane became symbolic of physicians. The heads of the canes were often hollow, filled with aromatic herbs to ward off foul odors and harmful vapors, and embellished with gold, silver, or ivory. A particularly elegant one, topped by engraved gold, belonged to Dr. John Radcliffe (1650-1714), the personal physician to King William III. A tradition began when Dr. Radcliffe bequeathed his cane in 1714 to Dr. Richard Mead (1673-1754), whom he deemed his "successor of outstanding merit." And thus this particular cane began its journey accompanying one eminent British physician, in succession, after another. The last was Dr. Matthew Baillie who attended King George III as he descended into madness some years after our successful revolution.[4] Dr. Baillie's widow eventually bequeathed the cane to the new Royal College of Physicians where it was deposited in a glass case in the library in 1825.

The cane might have been forgotten had it not been for Dr. William Macmichael. In 1827, he popularized the history of Dr. Radcliffe's cane in his book, *The Gold-Headed Cane*, an imaginative autobiography in the quirky voice of the cane.[5] The story recounts the observations and adventures of

Nancy Doyle with gold-headed cane, 1971,
courtesy of Nancy Doyle

the cane over 150 years as it tap-tap-tapped its way through history in the hands of six eminent English physicians. In the cane's own words, "I had, however, been closely connected with medicine for a century and a half; and might consequently, without vanity, look upon myself as the depository of many important secrets, in which the dignity of the profession was nearly concerned." Although, once the cane was retired to a glass case in the library, "...it was impossible to avoid secretly lamenting the obscurity which was henceforth to be my lot."

But no lamentations occurred. The anthropomorphic life of the cane crossed the Atlantic. In the land lost by King George, the cane came to embody not the eminence, but more the empathy, of a physician. Within a hundred years of its feared obscurity, the new world legacy of the cane continued its journey and traversed the North American continent to land at

UCSF with Dr. William J. Kerr, Professor and Chairman of the Department of Medicine. He established the UCSF Gold Headed Cane Society in 1939. Three students from each graduating class who exemplified the qualities of a "true physician" would be inducted at commencement into the Society, and one presented with an actual gold-headed cane.

The selection of the three students is egalitarian and democratic. Each member of the graduating class submits the names of up to three classmates. Faculty members familiar with the whole class then narrow the nominee group to three students. A final vote by the class selects the one person to be honored with the Gold Headed Cane. The cane recipient is held in suspense until announced at Commencement.

By 1971, many medical schools and professional medical organizations had similar Gold Headed Cane Societies. UCSF was not alone. But the events at the UCSF Society in 1971 made history for the entire nation. The recipient of the cane had never been a female—at UCSF or any other medical school or society. That all three nominees at UCSF in 1971 were female took this exception to an exponential level.

At Commencement, to the honor of our class of 1971 and the UCSF School of Medicine, Nancy received the Gold Headed Cane. Bonnie Vestal and Marie Feltin, the two other nominees, became members of the Society. As Nancy stood on the podium to accept the cane, she whispered to the Dean that she would like to speak. Previously no recipient had dared. Looking at her classmates, and at the whole wide audience of faculty, parents, and friends, she thought of the efforts of many in our class who had worked for greater equity for minority students in medicine and of others who had endeavored to help underserved members of the community. Then she said, "No one person can represent all of the qualities of a true physician, but collectively we represent the best of medicine. I am honored to accept the cane on behalf of our entire class of 1971." With these words, she started the tradition at UCSF of the recipient of the cane speaking at commencement.

Nancy, Bonnie, and Marie made Gold Headed Cane world history that day. The award recognized them, and they honored the Society. Newspapers across the country noted the event as did fellow Gold Headed Cane societies. And UCSF changed forever that day.

Nancy matched for internship at the Children's Hospital in Denver. She had great admiration for Dr. Arnold Silverman, Chief of Pediatric Gastroenterology at the hospital and under whom she previously worked as a visiting student doing a fourth-year externship. That rotation with Dr. Silverman had been prompted, in part, because her boyfriend (and future husband), George, was based in Denver for his final year of internal medicine residency.

Internships invariably were difficult, especially in the 1970s when no limits existed on the number of hours interns worked in training programs. Nancy's on-call schedule every other night entailed continuous work for thirty-six-to-forty-hour stretches, well past the point of exhaustion. "The year was all work, even every holiday. But I learned my patients were also in the hospital for the holidays. We celebrated together," she said. "I ate graham crackers with the kids. I learned so much. I have no regrets."

Nancy's advocacy did effect some changes in the program. Work hours for interns became capped at twenty-four-hour shifts. Most rewarding for her, though, was the well-baby clinic she started for the children of prostitutes. To fit the mothers' schedules, the clinic hours were in the middle of the night, from two to four a.m., and conducted in the emergency room on the nights when Nancy was on call. As Nancy said, "They, too, loved their children."

When Nancy started her internship, she and George had been dating for about six months. After one week together in Denver, he left in early July for Vietnam to begin his two years of military service in the Army as chief of medicine at the 95th Evacuation Hospital near Danang. He returned on a three-day leave in November. Fatefully, precipitously, they married before a justice of the peace. They told no one except Bonnie and Bob Vestal, both also in Denver for internships, and one other couple who accompanied them as witnesses.

Nancy returned to UCSF the next year to continue her pediatric residency with the relative ease of being on call only every third night. George returned from Danang to the coveted position of serving his second year of military duty at Letterman Hospital at the Presidio. Nancy remembered the year as fun, marred only by her significant illness with gastrointestinal inflammation requiring hospitalization. It turned out to be due to a bacterial infection with Yersinia enterocolitica (Yersinia mesenteric lymphadenitis) though initially misdiagnosed as inflammatory bowel disease.

Because her illness prevented her from signing up for the second year of pediatric residency, Nancy instead did a two-year pediatric immunology fellowship at UCSF under the direction of Arthur Ammann, MD. She and Dr. Diane Wara, a fellow in pediatric immunology, initiated a Pediatric Rheumatology Clinic at UCSF under the guidance of Dr. Ammann, one of the few such clinics in the nation. As a result, Nancy finished the program as a board-certified pediatrician with added expertise in rheumatological diseases of children. Few pediatricians in the nation could claim similar experience.

The last months of her fellowship entailed a happy condition that turned into a near disaster. Pregnant with her first child, Nancy remained at work with few complications. But, at delivery, unanticipated placenta previa resulted in significant hemorrhage that sent her into shock. Fortunately, all emergency measures were rapid and successful. Nancy and her baby son,

Matt, survived without complications. Two weeks later, she reported back to work in order to receive full credit for her fellowship. Though anemic from the hemorrhage, she soldiered on. Such were the rules then.

The next stop was Santa Rosa, an attractive, moderately small community with a population of around 65,000, a mere hour's drive north of San Francisco. Nancy embraced Santa Rosa from the first day and relinquished forever her peripatetic past. Upon moving there, she became the first female pediatrician in the city. But, before starting work, she rewarded herself with a year off to care for herself and baby Matt. Never again would she have such a luxury of time.

Because the Pediatric Rheumatology Clinic at UCSF received patients in consultation from a wide area in Northern California, including Santa Rosa, upon arrival Nancy knew most of the pediatricians in her new city. She also had a clear idea of which group of pediatricians she aspired to join. In 1976, she approached the four male pediatricians of the Pediatric Associates group with a proposal. She suggested that she join their group and work four to four-and-a-half days per week, including every Saturday morning, but take no night call. They agreed—with caveats. Though they would pay her malpractice insurance, her salary would include no benefits or continuing education time *AND* her salary would be $20 per hour. Nancy accepted. Her salary averaged $20,000 per year under this arrangement for almost the next *two decades*.

When I asked Nancy about the financial inequity of this situation, she said that she was grateful to be doing what she loved. It hurt her pride to be so poorly compensated, but George, she said, worked "about 100 hours per week." He was not available to help at home, and his practice was lucrative. In the end, she said she had no regrets since she was able to be home reliably for the family—though never on a Saturday morning. If she wanted a Saturday morning off, she needed to negotiate a trade with one of her partners on his terms—a half day off for her with a payback of working a full day during the week for him. Despite the financial issue, she liked the pediatricians with whom she worked, and she admired them professionally. "We were a team," she said with obvious pride and sincerity.

The financial situation changed dramatically in 1995. A senior male partner decided to work less and stop night call. He negotiated an arrangement with his male colleagues to be paid a percentage of his billings and to cover one Saturday morning per month. Nancy immediately negotiated equal treatment. Her salary tripled.

Nancy became well-known in the medical community of Santa Rosa. She loved the diagnostic challenges of her practice, but, primarily, she loved her patients. In addition to taking care of most of the children with autoimmune and rheumatological diseases, she acquired the reputation as the "go-to" pediatrician to solve difficult cases. In her profession, she found the perfect match for the warmth of her personality and the sharpness of her intellect. At the end of a day, she would often jokingly say to her husband, "I bet I received more hugs today than you did."

Nancy maintained close affiliation with UCSF. For twenty-five years, she taught medical students *pro bono* on their rotations at the UC Family Practice Clinic in Santa Rosa, and later, from 2000-2011, as a paid faculty member. Like her father, she was a born teacher and counselor.

Nancy did not escape the difficulties of balancing her roles as wife and mother with that of her profession. But in many ways, her joy and satisfaction in her pediatric practice gave her the confidence and emotional strength to care for her children and to fulfill her role as a wife.

Three years after Matt's birth in 1975, her daughter, Megan, was born. She described being a mother as the peak experience of her life. Especially with her firstborn, the moment of hearing his first cry "changed everything—being a mother was a total connection to the universe for me—an honor, a gift, a new direction in my life. The experience made me a better doctor, not only for children, but for helping me see the 'child' in every human I meet," Nancy wrote in 2017 in her brief autobiography for this project.

Yet the challenges of motherhood were great. Beginning in early infancy, Megan was chronically ill. She suffered from a childhood immunodeficiency disorder (prolonged hypogammaglobulinemia of infancy) with many infections, obstructive airway problems from enlarged tonsils and adenoids that interrupted her sleep, and chronic otitis media resulting in profound hearing loss requiring hearing aids by age three. For the first years of Megan's life, Nancy would be up with her all night. Fortunately she had the help of an older woman, Friede, who assisted in the care for both children throughout their childhoods. Friede came every morning at five a.m., and then spent the day with Matt and Megan. This arrangement allowed Nancy to sleep from five until eight a.m. before going to work at nine. The schedule, as exhausting as that of an internship, continued year after year.

As Megan grew older and suffered fewer infections, illness in other forms emerged. She had mononucleosis in high school and developed a difficult renal problem with chronic pain that required surgery in junior college. Nancy always remained by her side. She recognized the valiant efforts by Megan to carry her life forward and fight the depression that would often threaten to overcome her. "Megan tried so hard," Nancy told me. "She graduated from Sonoma State University cum laude." But Megan's life had one difficulty after another. Basically alone, Nancy carried the burden, never wavering in her efforts to help her daughter.

Despite difficulties, and no parents escape them, Nancy loved being a mother. Along with their children, Nancy and George progressively became integrated into community life in Santa Rosa. With a small group of close friends, Nancy and George were instrumental in starting an academically oriented, small private school in Santa Rosa in 1983, Sonoma Country Day School, that encompassed kindergarten through eighth grade. Matt joined its first pioneer class and Megan followed with attendance at the school from fourth through eighth grades. A few years later, Nancy reduced her volunteer activities somewhat in order to devote more time to her children, especially Matt. With his myriad of interests in the creative arts, especially in theatre, acting, and singing, and in sports, Matt had asked his parents to allow him to become a boarder at the Robert Louis Stevenson School in Pebble Beach. Substantial commutes to Pebble Beach to attend his performances and sporting events were added to Nancy's schedule.

Life with George introduced Nancy to pleasures and hardships, though not quite in equal measures. He was a whirlwind. Activities and ideas spun from him, some landing safely, others spiraling into space. Yet most people who knew him agreed that he was energetic, smart, a very good cardiologist, and well versed in a wide range of cultural and intellectual interests. That left Nancy with all the work of running their home and raising their children.

George had been born into medicine. His father, grandfather, uncle, and brother were all Tennesseans and each one a doctor. From childhood, he was amply exposed to literature, arts, and culture. Into Nancy's life, he introduced his love of fine dining and wine, symphony and opera, history and politics. Some characterized him as a "Renaissance man." He was the energy behind starting the John Ash and Company restaurant in 1984 in Santa Rosa though it brought him to near bankruptcy at one point. Later he joined the Board of Overseers of the conservative Hoover Institute at Stanford University and became Sonoma County program coordinator of the Commonwealth Club of California. With his childhood friend, Tor Hagen, he helped to found the Viking River Cruises. These activities coexisted with his active involvement as a cardiologist seeing patients and supporting cardiac surgery in Santa Rosa. He belonged to the American College of Cardiology as an active senior member serving on many of its committees.

Though Nancy loved many of the activities George incorporated into

Nancy Doyle and family, 2012, courtesy of Nancy Doyle

their lives, they added a layer of work and responsibility to her overburdened schedule. It was a dilemma. They entertained frequently hosting large dinners with interesting wines and stimulating guests. The organization of the evenings fell to Nancy. Cultural and political events in San Francisco offered excitement but infringed on family time. It was exhausting.

George progressively became a difficult person with whom to live. His requirements for lots of intellectual stimulation, a big social life, and much entertainment contrasted with Nancy's primary happiness derived from her children and patients. With his frequent scholarly references, George could unwittingly seem arrogant at times whereas Nancy, always being herself, was universally liked enormously. "But I always saw us as a team. I liked the people and activities he brought to my life," she told me. In her view, George was the intellect, she was the heart, of a large group of diverse and engaging friends that came to orbit their life in Santa Rosa.

In 2000, Nancy retired from Pediatric Associates to care for her parents, both nearly eighty years old and in poor health. She moved them to a comfortable home on a golf course in Santa Rosa. As in the beginning, their "unit of three" united, with roles reversed, but their love and peacefulness together unchanged. And together they had to learn new ways to say farewell. Nancy's eighty-one-year-old mother died in 2005 after fifteen months in hospice care. When the time came, she turned off her own oxygen with the same quiet courage she had shown throughout her life. Nancy's father lived for four more years, each day becoming gradually more frail. In 2009, he received last rites from a monsignor close to Nancy and him. The next day, the family gathered for a farewell party. In the end, after the others left, he died with Nancy, George, and Megan beside him. He was ninety-one.

The decade that included the deaths of her parents was full of loss for Nancy. Her daughter, Megan, had more major illnesses, both physical and emotional, and Nancy remained the primary person to care for her. Her dog died. She discovered George's affair with a female colleague. She and George divorced in 2013. Her asthma persisted. Her pulmonary function tests worsened.

"So much loss while trying to care for everyone made me understand, you only have each day—so much you can't control or make better. It moved me to acceptance that I can't fix everything," Nancy wrote in 2017.

Though not anticipated, Nancy found herself happy once her divorce was final. Her friends rallied around her. She made new friends independent of the activities that had been centered on George. She dated. A freshness of life enveloped her, somewhat free of the onus of fulfilling the many needs of others.

Nancy and George remained close friends during the years that included their divorce. Nancy said, "He became more introspective and made a valiant effort to try to improve himself. He became a more sensitive person." Importantly, he increased his efforts in caring for Megan which put them as a family—father, daughter, and Nancy—in close and regular contact after they ceased to live together. Nancy and George continued to share some of their former life such as their tickets to the San Francisco Opera.

Then one day in April, a year after their divorce, Nancy had trouble reaching George by telephone. She went to his home the next morning. There she found him, slumped in a living room chair, dead since the night before from a pulmonary embolus.

One of the findings that Lillian clearly documented in this study of women physicians was the difficulty imposed by having a child with special needs. This type of hardship comes as no surprise. Among the group, fourteen had children with physical handicaps, chronic illnesses, or emotional/mental difficulties. The challenges presented by such a child altered their lives forever, just as they did in Nancy's life.

My Career Saved Me

My childhood was prosaic. It had none of the hardships of Helene's or horrors of Marie's. It lacked the color and diversity of Faith's and Schumarry's, and the warmth of parental love of Nancy's and Rima's. My best word for it is boring. I craved some measure of excitement.

Both of my parents were stable and well-educated. In many ways, my family epitomized the post-WWII generation with breadwinner father, stay-at-home mother, three-child household aimed at financial security and upward mobility.

The men in my father's family came from a long line of ministers, variously Lutheran or Presbyterian or Baptist, with my grandfather eventually landing in Los Angeles in the 1920s. Born in 1909, my father had three younger sisters. From the little I gleaned of his childhood, it was devout and strict. On Sundays, attending church and reading the Bible were the only allowed activities. Even doing homework, playing his French horn, and reading non-religious literature were forbidden. His mother died when he was twelve. I always attributed his quiet, almost silent personality to his upbringing. With his sharp, analytical mind, he had a successful college career at the California Institute of Technology (Caltech) overlapping briefly with Albert Einstein. To earn extra money in college, he played his French horn at dances.

My mother's family was a little more colorful. Her parents also made their way from the Midwest to Los Angeles, where my mother was born in 1911, the oldest of four children. Her gregarious, pool-playing father, somewhat full of schemes and many prejudices against Mexicans, worked as a jeweler. He took advantage of the WPA-sponsored programs to start a modest jewelry school in the 1930s. Though neither parents had one, the attainment of a college education for each of the children was a primary goal of the family. My mother went to UCLA, majored in botany, then became a high school English teacher as did her sister, the next sibling in line. Each returned her earnings to the family in order to finance the college educations of their two brothers. Throughout her life, my mother was immeasurably proud of having had a university education.

My parents met and married in the depth of the Great Depression. The scarcity of those years irreversibly marked my mother. Throughout her long life, she would save zippers from worn-out clothes for reuse, fill closets with extra bags of sugar or flour bought on sale, write in the margin of a letter to save paper, and follow many similar habits as a hedge against another financial disaster.

For the first five years of married life, my mother taught high school and continued to send her paycheck to her parents. When my older sister was born in 1939, I think my mother regretted having to leave her job. My chemical engineer father worked for Standard Oil Company of California (later Chevron) "cracking petroleum" as he explained if questioned. As part of a vital, war-related industry, he remained a civilian throughout WWII. My mother indulged her love of botany and gardening throughout the war with Victory Gardens.

And so it came to pass that my parents survived the Depression and WWII with hardship that was real but, in the context of the times, minor. I was born three years after my sister in 1942, and my brother arrived fifteen months later, in 1944. When I was five, my father was transferred to Chevron's headquarters in San Francisco. After five years in the fog of San Francisco, we moved north to the sun of San Anselmo in Marin County for the benefit of my mother's gardening interests.

The myth that middle children inhabit the thorny seat in sibling hierarchy did not hold for me. My older sister fought constantly with my parents. I watched and laid low. Once I finally had a bedroom of my own, I retreated behind its closed door and devoured books while warfare raged beyond my bunker. From my sister's travails, I learned what to avoid, how to glide below the radar, and the art of keeping to myself.

The lessons I learned were to do well in school, make no trouble, and plot my escape. Fortunately my natural inclination made enactment of those lessons quite doable. I liked school, especially science and history. At heart, I was not a troublemaker. And reading book after book after book, safely sequestered in my room, gave me a clear vision of a potential outside world that could contain excitement and an independent life for me. In book after book, I even developed the notion that being a doctor would be grand.

And so my escape came in the form of college. In this, my parents were generous. They allowed me to consider any school in the US and offered fully to finance my education. In choosing where to apply, I first eliminated any school that had the Greek system of sororities and fraternities. Three years earlier, I had watched with horror as my sister went through that ordeal which seemed to me like an elitist cattle call. With that slice of schools eliminated, a glance at a map made my decision easy. Boston—as distant from San Anselmo as I could get in continental USA. Moreover, as a girl who had never been out of California, Boston sounded terrific to me. In September of 1960, I clutched my Grasshopper suitcase, boarded a plane for the second time in my life, and flew to Logan Airport. It was raining when I arrived, but, through a combination of the MTA subway and bus, wet and excited, I found my way to Wellesley College. I was free at last.

Wellesley was decidedly not San Anselmo. It took some adjustment. It was a private women's college, whereas my entire previous educational experience had been at coeducational public schools. I had not had a close girlfriend since early grammar school. My home in San Anselmo was in a neighborhood with no children near to me in age. In high school, my best friend had been my boyfriend. To my surprise, I learned at Wellesley that I could make close female friends. To this day, my closest friends on this planet remain my friends from college.

Wellesley exposed me to an intellectual universe that I had not known existed. Courses in art history, philosophy, English literature, poetry—including one devoted solely to T.S. Eliot—politics, economics, and even the required one in Biblical history, opened worlds to me. Of course, I took a vast amount of science compared to most of my classmates. Wellesley had no premed advisor, but it was not difficult to determine what courses were needed. To counteract the sneaking fear that medical school existed only in my imagination, I majored in mathematics thinking that was a safe bet for employment after college. In financing my expensive education at Wellesley, my father had made it abundantly clear to me that I was off the payroll at graduation.

Other conflicts lurked in my psyche. Throughout my boring childhood, I missed adventure. Skiing was as close as I had come. I always loved the thought of flying, however out of reach that possibility was. With some students at Harvard and MIT, I came close. We jumped out of airplanes.

Susan Detweiler, 1968, courtesy of the author

We went to the grass airfield in Concord, packed our own WWII-surplus parachutes, and took turns jumping out of Cessnas at 3,000 feet. It was crazy. I thought it was fun. I rode motorcycles. I learned to shoot a shotgun.

Though I had some boyfriends in college, nothing was serious until I visited Nashville during my senior year. One of my roommates who lived there suggested I stop over briefly on my way to California for Christmas. Nashville would be full of holiday parties. She assured me I would have fun. For the first party, my escort, Franklin, was an ex-Navy fighter pilot who owned an open-cockpit Stearman biplane. He was eleven years older than I. He took me flying the next day—and thereafter pursued me like an escaping Japanese Zero. It was flattering. It was exciting. Nashville publicized him as its most eligible bachelor. I resisted for a year, then agreed to marry him. Though I moved to Nashville, a southern lady I was not. I enrolled in Vanderbilt and took courses in anatomy, organic chemistry, and statistics. I earned my pilot's license and spent hours cruising over the rolling hills of Tennessee. I worked in the research laboratory of Dr. Paine, the Chief of Medicine at the Nashville VA Hospital. And I applied to medical schools, including Vanderbilt and UCSF. As I made plans to start in the fall, Franklin and I agreed that we had little in common beyond fast planes and fast cars. In the summer of 1967, we divorced on good terms after two and a half years of marriage. Almost immediately, I left for San Francisco.

Nonetheless I blamed myself for poor judgment and was ashamed. I branded myself with a scarlet D, a divorcée at twenty-four.

In my four years of medical school at UCSF, I never once lost my thrill of being there. Of course, it entailed a huge amount of work, but that was the nature of the beast. No one expected it to be easy. Of the clinical rotations, I liked surgery at San Francisco General Hospital the best where I spent the majority of my fourth year. I loved the rawness of the problems and the complete spectrum of humanity passing through the hospital's doors. My courage failed me, though, in trying for a surgical internship. Surgery was then too much of a samurai culture for me.

The social and political turmoil of the late '60s did not leave me untouched. One of the benefits of starting college in 1960 had been to live in the brief magic of the Kennedy administration, however naively I saw it as an eighteen-to-twenty-one-year-old. And then, in what felt like an instant, to watch the hope and idealism of that moment shatter. Once back in San Francisco, I joined political activists against the Vietnam War. Medical students and faculty together, we would meet on top of Millberry Union, paint anti-war signs, don our white coats, and march down Fell

Street to City Hall. It was a heady time. Mixed with the anti-war protests was the ever-present knowledge that most of the young (male) physicians were headed to military service.

Entwined in the dilemma of this era, I began a relationship with a young physician, Laird, who arrived at UCSF from Harvard for internship and residency in internal medicine. We shared many mutual interests in literature, sports, friends, and politics. We even looked somewhat alike in a clean-cut, all-American way. On the eve of his departure for his share of Vietnam War military service in the US Army, like Nancy and George, we married before a Justice of the Peace with two friends as witnesses. It was an impulsive decision.

I continued at UCSF in pediatrics for internship. My thoughts centered on doing pediatric hematology and oncology. In the early 1970s, initial success in treating leukemias in children and bone marrow transplantation were transforming the specialty in exciting ways. Dr. Louis Diamond, a faculty member widely acclaimed as the father of pediatric hematology, took me under his wing that year. Whenever I had an hour of free time, I would seek him out to look at bone marrow specimens with him. On the glass slides under the microscope, the whole disease unfolded. It seemed to me that everything with respect to the diagnosis, the treatment, and the likely outcome of the disease was derivative of what one discerned on the slide. It didn't take me long to discover that I liked making the diagnosis more than treating the disease.

I finished my internship and transferred to a pathology residency.

Pathology proved to be a perfect choice. The specialty combined the dissection of surgery with the visual elegance of seeing disease in its most elemental state—the actual cells forming the disease. In a malignant disease, you could follow the deranged cells as marauders through normal tissue. In inflammatory diseases, the cells of the immune systems swarmed through the target areas. In various benign diseases, the altered patterns of growth were the clues to the condition in question. The whole human body and many of its ailments became displayed through the microscope. I found it exciting.

I stayed at UCSF for my first year of training in pathology. During these years, Laird finished his military duty, then returned to UCSF and completed his internal medicine residency. In 1973, we moved to Boston. I transferred to the Massachusetts General Hospital for my next three years of pathology residency, and Laird did a neurology residency at the Brigham Hospital. The birth of our son, Aaron, was the one truly happy event of those three years.

I loved my training at the MGH and the extra opportunities it afforded. As the liaison resident for the Lymphoma Clinic, I participated in additional training in hematopathology and the relevant special techniques used for diagnosis in lymphomas and leukemias. I had extra training in skin pathology that subsequently allowed me to take dermatopathology subspecialty boards.

But the Boston/Harvard programs had their conservative side. At the MGH, only one female at a time was allowed in the four-year residency program in pathology. In this regard, my best moment arrived shortly before the birth of my son. In the pathology department, specimens were divided into the "large side," meaning larger resection specimens like breasts or colons or kidneys, and the "small side," such as small skin or liver or brain biopsies. One day when I was the resident handling the large specimens, a senior and very patrician surgeon, Dr. Raker, marched into the laboratory and demanded in a stentorian voice, "Who is the man on the large side?" He had with him a large resection of a melanoma; he wished to explain the orientation of the margins. I was sitting with my back to him. In his commanding presence, I stood, swung my pregnant abdomen toward him, and announced, "I am the man on the large side." We became instant friends.

Susan Detweiler, 1995, courtesy of the author

In 1976, shortly before Boston's bicentennial events of the Declaration of Independence, Laird, two-year old Aaron, and I departed Boston for Seattle. Our daughter, Aaron's baby sister, Amanda, arrived in September.

In January of 1977, I started my first job as a surgical pathologist at the University of Washington Medical Center. Three years later, realizing that advancement would be slow without a dominant interest in research, I switched to join the Virginia Mason Medical Center in downtown Seattle. Founded as a partnership in 1920, Virginia Mason was primarily a referral hospital and clinic for specialty care in the northwest. It was also definitely an all-boys club. When I joined, I was the only female physician on the staff and became the first female partner in 1983. I stayed for twenty-eight years.

My practice at Virginia Mason was ideal for my interests. The institution was full of medical and surgical specialists who kindly provided pathology with endlessly interesting cases. In the laboratory we developed all of the ancillary tools we needed for diagnostic sophistication. We were a group of six pathologists and, though we considered ourselves general surgical pathologists, we each had subspecialty interests. I did most of the skin pathology and passed my subspecialty boards in Dermatopathology in 1983. One colleague and I ran the hematopathology portion of our practice. We served on the tumor boards for the hospital and ran many continuing medical education programs.

In addition, being supportive to the institution as a whole was important. For over twenty years I was the head of the Quality Assurance Committee and a member of the Professional Liability Committee. As the first female on the staff, the Personnel Committee recruited me early on. I was a key member of the group that established the principles of continuous quality improvement into the operational structure of Virginia Mason. Along the way, I was the first female president of the Pacific Northwest Society of Pathology.

At the end of 2007, on the day I turned sixty-five, I retired from my full-time practice at Virginia Mason. After that, I worked until 2014 on a part-time basis at the University of Washington and Group Health Cooperative (now Kaiser) with a practice restricted to Dermatopatholoy.

In looking back, I think the thirty-seven years of my practice included the golden age of medicine. Huge and exciting advances in medical knowledge occurred, and the burdensome financial and bureaucratic onus had yet to descend in earnest.

I loved being a mother to my son and daughter. And juggling a career and parenthood worked out quite well for me. I hired a series of wonderful women to help with childcare. Though I basically had no extra time to read or indulge myself, that was okay with me. The joy of being with my children more than offset any sacrifice of private time.

Laird participated little in the work of running the household though he was clever at wood working and building things. What divided us was his constant complaining. Over the years, his complaints covered everything. Initially his obligation to perform his military service earned the brunt of his displeasure. I could understand that. We were both against the war in Vietnam. Later his umbrage fell on Boston—the weather, the city, the demands of his residency. Then his resentment migrated to his job as a neurologist in Seattle—he had to work too hard.

I did not escape his rants. My judgment was questioned because of my earlier failed marriage. My statements to counter the causes of his complaints proved my inability to understand the inequity under which he lived. He claimed he should be spared any domestic responsibility because he had to work harder as a neurologist than I did as a pathologist. He came near to rage because pathologists were paid more than neurologists. That I had blond streaks put in my hair and wore contact lenses proved my vain superficiality and poor character compared to his midwestern integrity.

The complaints went on and on and on. To a great extent, it mystified me why he remained so unhappy. We had good jobs, two wonderful, healthy children, and an interesting life in a marvelous city near mountains and sea. People thought us a picture-perfect family. It was confusing, too. In a group, Laird could be outgoing and funny. His intellect and verbal adeptness were impressive.

I retreated into silence. No words I uttered blunted his resentment at seemingly every facet of our lives together.

Then one day in 1984, after fourteen years of marriage, Laird told me the truth. He was transgender. From his earliest three-year-old memory, he wanted to be a girl. He begged me to keep his secret.

I was stunned. Then relieved. His unhappiness and anger were not my fault.

It took me some time to decide what to do. I waited until my children were safely in college in Boston, as far away as possible from the fallout that would take place when Laird became openly transgender. I divorced him in 1996. I felt released from prison for a crime I did not commit.

My future then acquired a wonderful chapter. My long-time friend, Alexander Clowes, a vascular surgeon at the University of Washington whom I knew from our mutual interest in music, and I became a couple after he was widowed in 1998. He loved my children from the beginning, and they grew to love him. The four of us stood together as Alec and I married in 2000. We had fifteen glorious years together. For the first time, I experienced the joy of intimacy and love—and peace. The real tragedy of my life was Alec's death in 2015 from a glioblastoma.

I have spent years pondering why I made the mistake of marrying Laird. I count it as the big mistake of my life. Most likely it was the congruence of multiple factors, not least of which were the exigencies of the Vietnam War.

I do know for certain that my profession saved me. My success as a pathologist gave me self-confidence and a steadiness that grounded me as I faced dealing with Laird's transgender identity becoming public and the impact the news would have on my teenage children in the 1980s and '90s. In my judgment, it meant waiting until they were adults to divorce him, and, in the interim, maintaining a stable home. Once my D-Day timing approached, I planned it like Operation Overlord, down to the day, almost the hour, when I would start the process. Methodical. Like preparing for an

Susan Detweiler and Nancy Doyle, 2016, by permission of Nancy Doyle and
the author

exam or assembling the facts for a lecture or difficult diagnosis.

For Nancy, her problem differed. Her daughter presented a life-long
illness which could have overwhelmed most people. Nancy faced helping
her daughter mostly alone while fulfilling many other complicated tasks
presented by George's many interests and later the issues of their divorce.
Yet she managed, year after year.

Nancy does not credit her profession for her ability to carry her burdens.
Rather, she attributes it to her military upbringing and being raised by her

parents. Everything in their backgrounds and shared life in the military trained them to deal with disasters and to surmount hardships. Their enduring message remained—no matter what happens, you keep going, you rely on yourself, you persevere. And, to a large extent, you do not ask for help though you readily extend help to others. Through their closeness as a family of three, their message endures in Nancy. Grit, determination, and resilience.

Still Nancy's self-confidence as a pediatrician and the emotional rewards she continues to receive from her young patients help to sustain her optimism as she grapples with the complex and poorly understood illnesses that plague her daughter. Entwined with Megan in irrevocable bonds, Nancy will never abandon her efforts to help her daughter. Grit, determination, resilience, and enduring love.

CHAPTER 7

ALTERNATE CAREER PATHWAYS

By 1975 when Lillian traveled the country for the Time 2 follow-up, all of the newly minted physicians in the study had finished their internships. The vast majority were either in residencies or the early phase of working in the medical fields they would pursue for their careers. It had been a long pull. To arrive at this point, the mean age of the women hovered around thirty-three, and their educational commitment encompassed between twenty-one to more than thirty years. One third of the women (33%) soldiered on from internship to residency or first job without a break. Faith Fitzgerald, Rima McLeod, and Bonnie Vestal were among those who marched onward, looking neither left nor right, straight into residencies. Many of the women (57%) were slightly kinder to themselves and paused for a break, usually lasting less than six months, before continuing training or taking positions that they then followed for the majority of their careers.

Five women (9%) followed career routes that were unusual compared to the majority of physicians within this cohort.

After a delay of seven years, one woman did an ophthalmology residency. Though she retained her license to practice medicine in California, her interests changed to midwifery. She became a midwife herself and went on to train others in that profession. She received many awards for her work. Another woman completed a pediatric residency after a seven-year delay and then quit medicine for personal reasons. A third woman left because she felt she "never fit into medicine." Instead she started a successful book-keeping service in rural Hawaii. In addition, one physician who began her career without delay ultimately retired before 1990 for personal reasons.

Finally, one physician, lost to follow-up, quit for unknown reasons.

Two physicians, both of whom eventually had highly successful careers, followed paths which were unusual within the group. Their careers illustrate the successful possibility of emphasizing one area of life and then later another area. Dr. Norma McKenzie (Schmitt) and Dr. Tomoko Inadomi Hooper both followed a flexible approach to their careers and, to a degree, reinvented themselves over time. Their initial primary commitment was raising their children. They bypassed the heavy, inflexible demands of further training in residencies, fellowships, and other rigid career commitments while their children were young. Once their children gained degrees of independence, the priorities of the women changed. After internship, Norma worked for nearly eleven years in outpatient settings, which she enjoyed and in which she gained valuable experience while having reasonable control over her schedule, before she declared "it's my time now" and started her psychiatry residency. Tomoko paused her career after internship for fourteen years before she charged ahead ultimately to become a Professor of Preventative Medicine and Biometrics at the Uniform Services University. Both women switched careers. As Norma said, "I believe one can have it all but not necessarily all at once. I did not take the straight path to the top but chose the scenic route." Personal tragedies, by contrast, propelled Tomoko into a career for which she had almost silently prepared.

It's My Time Now; It's Only Fair

As with many of my interviews, I did not know what to expect as I drove south on the Virginia highway from Charlottesville to Richmond to meet with Norma. And, as with many of my female classmates, Norma and I had less than a bare acquaintance from medical school. Neither of us would have recognized each other in a police lineup. Yet, as with each meeting for this project, our shared experience at UCSF served as a platform for an honest

Norma McKenzie, 1971, courtesy of Norma McKenzie

and revealing exchange of life stories. At the end of the afternoon as I drove to the airport, I realized Norma possessed the fortunate combination of both understanding herself from an early age and abundant common sense. At each stage of her life, she was rational about her choices and decisive in her decisions.

In the scheme of assessment of family economic and social status commonly used in psychology in the 1960s, Norma's parents would have been classified as providing a high socioeconomic background for their children. Without question, they created a family life extraordinarily high in warmth, nurture, and stability for Norma and her younger brother. Both parents graduated from the University of Nevada, her mother in home economics and her father in civil engineering. They supported their children in pursuing whatever educational and career aspirations Norma and her brother desired.

In her early childhood, Norma's family moved to Concord, California. She and her brother attended public schools. For college, Norma received a California State Scholarship and selected Stanford University. Caltech was the only school to reject her application and, reflecting the prejudice of the times, informed her that her gender did not fit their student profile. Their pronouncement was not the last time Norma would hear such a judgment.

Norma's life-long fascination with the human brain began at Stanford. How does a person learn? Though not obvious at the time, her entire professional life circled that question. She majored in biology and psychology and left Stanford expecting to go to graduate school. "No one from Stanford just goes to work," she said as though it were an implicit understanding from Stanford that pertained to its graduates.

Norma took the mandate to heart. Driven by her interest in the brain, Norma received a two-year stipend for research at the University of Oregon. It was not a happy fit. At their first meeting, her assigned mentor informed her that "women do not have the kind of brain suitable for research." Nonetheless she persisted, earned a master's degree in physiology, and quickly departed Eugene for San Francisco and UCSF.

In order partially to finance her four years at UCSF, Norma enrolled in the school's work-study program. Although her paid work entailed participation in various tasks at the school, it added to the heavy academic burden of medical school. Her life became a blur of study and work with little time for social activities and none for fun. Once the blur somewhat condensed, she found she liked internal medicine and disliked surgery.

Norma's paid work at UCSF proved to influence her decisions and subsequent career more than the medical school curriculum. Most of her work assignments took place at the Langley Porter Psychiatric Institute.

As the first such institute in California, Langley Porter consisted of a psychiatric teaching hospital and an outpatient clinic, administered by the UCSF Department of Psychiatry and located on the main UCSF campus. It was an important part of UCSF and a dominant influence in psychiatry on the West Coast. For one of her jobs, Norma worked in the outpatient clinic for children where many of the young patients were autistic. At the time, the approach of the Institute focused on deficiencies of parenting, especially mothering, as causative for the child's condition. Norma was appalled. It seemed obvious to her that something biological was at play in the children, not bad mothering. The experience significantly cooled her interest in psychiatry.

In addition, a tragic event during medical school landed closer to Norma's personal life. Norma shared an apartment and close friendship with a woman in our class, Vivian Balch, a talented, kind, dedicated student who suffered from depression. She committed suicide during our third year. "Her depression was an illness, and it was an illness that killed her," Norma said. Her suicide shocked everyone in our class. What surprises me to this day is that the school remained silent. There was no attempt by the administration to help our class, or Norma, process her death or acknowledge our sadness and confusion. Such were the times in 1968.

Norma matched for an internal medicine internship at Highland Hospital in Oakland. As each of us learned, internship was a brutal, exhausting, and maturing year. For Norma, yet another tragedy added to her burden. Her father died. After building a successful career and shepherding his family, he died at sixty of coronary artery disease. He had always worked hard, pushed aside leisure, and postponed future pleasure to accomplish the tasks of the present. Norma saw much of her life reflected in his. She decided not to continue with residency training in favor of an easier schedule with the possibility of some free time, a reasonable salary, and even some fun.

It was a pivotal decision. It changed her life. It became her style.

Norma's boyfriend in medical school was our classmate, Jim Schmitt. Though he and Norma had parted ways during internship, they reunited afterward and married in 1973. Jim continued with his internal medicine residency at Highland Hospital, and Norma worked in its outpatient clinic.

As with all of the men in medical school at the time, at the conclusion of his residency, Jim faced military service. He additionally owed two extra years in return for his ROTC scholarship that had financed his undergraduate years at UC Berkeley. Norma and Jim moved to Wichita Falls and became reluctant Texans from 1975 until 1979 for Jim's assignment as an internist at the Sheppard Air Force Base Hospital. Norma also joined the hospital's staff in the outpatient medical clinic. Their son, Eric, was born there in 1975.

Norma and Jim failed to bond with Texas. They left immediately after the four years and returned to Norma's home base in Concord, California. What Norma did bond with was motherhood. She loved her role as an active, attentive mother on the model of her own childhood. Eric and his younger brother, Brian, born in 1979, thrived. Norma and Jim agreed that their family was their first priority in life and their basis for every major decision.

For the next four years in Concord, from 1979 until 1983, Jim first commuted to UCSF for an endocrinology fellowship and then to the Naval hospital in Oakland to work as an internist. Norma returned to outpatient work, this time at the UC Berkeley Student Health Service working with the students on health matters and counseling them, a job she enjoyed and found to be an ideal way to combine her roles as parent and professional with built-in flexibility and some free time.

Then came 1983. Eleven years had passed since internship. Norma and

Jim had two active, healthy, and school-age boys, Eric in third grade and Brian in kindergarten. The exigencies of Jim's obligations and career that had previously dictated their moves and options were completed.

Norma announced, "It's my time now. It's only fair." Her interest in psychiatry had revived. The shape of their future clarified.

They moved to Richmond, Virginia, home to the Medical College of Virginia. Norma began a residency in psychiatry. Jim became the parent with primary responsibility for the children. Their roles reversed. Jim worked part-time in internal medicine at the Richmond VA Hospital which was run by the medical school. (After Norma finished her residency, Jim increased to full-time at the VA Hospital and later became Chief of Medicine.) Norma and Jim were in firm agreement that their "family was the important thing" and that one of them should always be available for the boys. For the next three years, Jim graduated to that role. He did it well, and he did it willingly.

Norma loved psychiatry. In retrospect, she wished she had entered earlier so she could have been part of the transition to the profession's new biological approach to mental disease. Psychiatry had largely discarded the Freudian theories based on unconscious conflicts and psychosexual development as the cause of mental illness that she had encountered, and rejected, in medical school at Langley Porter. For Norma, the key point was that the brain makes behavior. Abnormalities in the brain caused the abnormal behaviors identified as mental disorders. Her formal entrance into psychiatry stimulated the pent-up curiosity she had harbored since college about the biological functioning of the brain, now further enhanced by the pleasure she experienced with patient interaction. Furthermore, and unlike most psychiatrists, Norma had ten years of general medical experience. She could identify abnormal, nonpsychotic behavior caused by strictly medical problems and not be misled into an incorrect conclusion. Psychiatry was her perfect fit.

After residency, Norma joined the Medical College of Virginia as a full-time faculty member in the Department of Psychiatry. She described herself as a "jack of all trades," variously running the inpatient service, overseeing the emergency psychiatric service, and, additionally, caring for private patients. She had a full academic load. She taught medical students and residents, gave lectures, ran conferences, and wrote papers.

As her career progressed, Norma gravitated to addressing mental illnesses afflicting the disadvantaged segments of society. As a self-described "in the trenches kind of person," she became an excellent fit for mental health work in Congressional District 19, a district near Richmond that was rural and poor with a disproportionate amount of mental illness and substance abuse. The state's mental hospital was adjacent to the district. After discharge, many of the hospital's patients remained nearby for ongoing treatment. Norma became the Medical Director of the District 19 Community Services Board, a faculty position within the medical school. She found great pleasure in meeting the needs of this challenging population. Devising treatment strategies for them appealed to her problem-solving instincts. The patient population also offered unlimited teaching possibilities for her students and residents.

No practice in the region was more "in the trenches." For example, three of Norma's patients during her years directing outpatient psychiatric care at District 19 were murderers. She smiled broadly at me in describing them. They were among her favorites. All three were schizophrenics and had been adjudicated not guilty by reason of insanity. As Norma said, "They were the sweetest men you would ever meet when they were on their meds." Moreover, "They always took their meds. They were terrified of going back to their former state."

One of Norma's great frustrations in working with the District 19 population was political and concerned the state's disability system. When patients were actively ill, for example with bipolar disorder or schizophrenia, they could be enrolled in the state's disability program and be able to afford their medications. But, once on medication and functioning well enough to find employment, they would lose their disability rating. Often they then could not afford their meds, would relapse, and lose their job. It was a perverse cycle that made no sense. Norma did her best to handle the problem politically, but it remained an uphill battle.

Political problems aside, Norma counted her years as medical director of District 19 as the best part of her career. She kept the job until her retirement at sixty-five.

When immersed in the everyday fray, perspective on one's career can be difficult. Now after her retirement, I asked Norma about her insights, especially as a female physician with a ten-year gap before practicing full-time in her specialty.

By the 1980s, after her long interval between her internship and psychiatry residency, Norma felt female physicians were more able to be themselves. In the 1970s, medicine was basically a male profession. Women saw themselves in that reflection, and, in a sense, had to outdo the image. As a female, you not only found yourself acting like your male colleagues, but overdoing it in order to guarantee your right to be there. When Norma returned in 1983, changes had occurred in both male and female residents. "Women no longer had to act masculine, they could be more themselves and attentive to the emotional side," she said. And, ten years later, it was easier to find female mentors within the profession. She also judged men to be more open to viewing women as colleagues than previously.

With respect to salaries, change had been slower. Norma accepted the salary that the Medical College of Virginia offered her. Much later she discovered that her male colleagues usually negotiated their salaries to a higher level in order to cover any gap in pay they might suffer due to unremunerative work they performed as part of their job. Norma suffered in this regard. She added extra work to her schedule by caring for private

Norma McKenzie, recent photo,
courtesy of Norma McKenzie

patients who could pay to compensate for her time with her indigent patients. The institution required this. A similar situation existed with the possibility of sanctuary time for research. Norma did not imply that the medical school deliberately mistreated her. Rather, she wished she had had a mentor in the beginning who could have given her guidance in negotiating better salary and research options.

Prepared—When Life Changed

Tomoko Inadomi Hooper was born in 1944 at the Tule Lake internment camp in Northern California, officially the Tule Lake War Relocation Center. To Tomoko it was always "the camp." The area contained the largest of the WWII concentration-segregation centers for Japanese Americans and

Japanese nationals after May of 1942. Later a nearby prisoner-of-war camp for German and Italian soldiers was added. This scarred, implacable land was loaded with bloody history and dislocation. Its Indigenous people, the tiny Modoc Tribe, first encountered the US Army in the 1843 expedition led by Captain Fremont. Their sad history progressed to The Modoc War in 1873 when a band of fifty-two Modoc warriors fought the US Army in the nearby lava beds.[1] After their defeat and the execution of four tribal leaders, the few remaining Modocs endured forced relocation to the designated Indian Territory, then a region of the Louisiana Purchase that later became part of the state of Oklahoma.*

Tomoko remembers that her father, an American citizen born in Honolulu, Hawaii, found himself, at least initially, in the distrusted group of men of Japanese ancestry at Tule Lake. Both *Issei* (first-generation immigrants born in Japan) and *Nisei* (second-generation Japanese Americans born in the US) men faced questions in the camps about their loyalty to the United States. The distrust of Tomoko's father arose from his answers— that he had traveled to Japan in the past and might travel there in the future to visit his relatives. Tomoko's father did not realize that his answers would be considered suspicious in light of the heightened fear of espionage at the time. Later, as the war wore on, her father managed to clarify his answers and reduce doubts as to his American allegiance.

Like Chiura Obata, the renowned artist from Berkeley, Tomoko's parents had first lived in the horse stalls at the Tanforan Race Tracks, a site south of San Francisco used as an assembly center while the Tule Lake Camp underwent construction. During internment, Tomoko's parents met,

---

* John Yoo as Deputy Assistant US Attorney General at the Office of Legal Counsel cited the Supreme Court's Modoc ruling to argue that the USA was entitled to torture captives apprehended in Afghanistan because they, like Indians, were not entitled to be considered lawful combatants.[2]

married, and had two children.

After the war, her parents returned to the San Francisco Bay Area and bought a house in Berkeley with the help of an uncle. In her interview with Lillian when she was at UCSF, Tomoko described her parents as warm and loving. They passed their core values of hard work and the advantages of education to their children. At the time of their first meeting, Tomoko seemed young and innocent with a natural modesty to Lillian. Tomoko would probably have agreed. She remembered being a skinny child until she was ten. Sensitive and shy, she felt that the internment and her parents' memories of "watch dogs and centurions with guns" left their mark on her. At the same time, her parents never expressed bitterness about their internment. Rather, they promoted the precepts of assimilation: you live in a white man's society, you must behave; because your physical appearance as Asian singles you out, you can never really fit in; therefore, you must try harder, you must be better than average. Do not make waves.

At home, her family mostly spoke English, throwing in only occasional words in Japanese such as *gohan* instead of rice, although Japanese was always her father's primary language. Her parents enrolled her in after-school Japanese language classes while living in Berkeley during elementary school. Later, in college, when she decided to learn more about her Japanese heritage, these earlier classes gave her a good foundation in the Japanese language.

Tomoko and her family moved to Castro Valley, eighteen miles south of Berkeley, shortly after she started junior high school in the mid-1950s.[3] Castro Valley then was a rural, unincorporated, predominantly agricultural, solidly white community historically known for its many chicken ranches and tomato fields.[4] There her father developed a successful retail nursery business on an acre of land he purchased on Castro Valley Boulevard, the region's main street. He combined his extensive knowledge of plants with his aesthetic of landscaping to create an atmosphere of a Japanese garden in the nursery. The plants and specimen trees in the retail portion of his business were interspersed with attractive plant displays and integrated with a waterfall and koi pond. Tomoko remembered him spending hours in the meticulous art of growing bonsai trees and shrubs—removing dirt around roots of the plants with chopsticks and carefully pruning the roots before repotting. His reputation spread. Soon he was one of the region's bonsai experts and became one of the first two *senseis* (teachers) of the Yamato Bonsai Kai, a club founded in 1969 in San Lorenzo.[5] The Golden State Bonsai Federation honored him with *The Circle of Sensei Award* in 2009, the equivalent of a lifetime achievement award.[6] And, perhaps best of all, one of his favorite bonsai trees lives today in the renowned Bonsai Garden of Lake Merritt, labeled "Tree 161, Japanese black pine, started by seed in 1955, donated by Jimmy Inadomi, long-time president of Fuji Bonsai Club of Oakland."[7] Throughout her life, Tomoko has remained impressed with and enormously proud of her father's accomplishments. In addition to his gardening talent, he taught himself how to run a business, not only how to comply with state and federal rules and regulations, but also how to market his nursery and incorporate it into the community. Over the years, he became well-known in the East Bay region for the artistry of his landscaping with a clientele in wealthy neighborhoods of nearby Oakland and Berkeley.

Though shy, Tomoko was academically successful, earned good grades, and was well-liked by her peers. Moreover, she was drawn to challenges. In her predominantly all-white high school in Castro Valley, she was elected class president in her sophomore and junior years and student body president in her senior year.

For college, she selected UC Davis for the first two years, then transferred to UC Berkeley for her junior year. For her senior year, Tomoko made a bold decision which did not please her father. She opted for the study abroad program at UC Berkeley and enrolled in its affiliated college in Japan, the International Christian University in Tokyo.[8]

The International Christian University (ICU), a private, nondenominational, liberal arts institution, was established shortly after World War II on the founding principles of reconciliation and peace. The institution was bilingual with courses taught in either English or Japanese depending on the subject matter. Tomoko wished to immerse herself in the Japanese language and culture as a way to explore her ancestry. This involved an academic trade-off since ICU's science curriculum was far inferior to that of UC Berkeley. However, at that point in her education, Tomoko was unsure how she wished to apply her major in biological science. In the end, she impressed her father with her ability to write fluently in Japanese after only ten months in Tokyo. Though she had hopped around over the four years, she became the first member of her immediate and extended family to attain a university education. Furthermore she received a full University of California Regents Scholarship to attend UCSF, a high honor and an award that covered tuition, room, and board for the four years of medical school. This further impressed her father.

When Lillian asked Tomoko about her motivation for medicine, she said, "This is hard for me to explain. I didn't consider it until my junior year in college. I thought I would enter an art career. Perhaps as a medical illustrator. No one in my family was in medicine. I met premed students at UC Berkeley, so I applied to medical school along with the schools of pharmacy and physical therapy to take advantage of my undergraduate science background. Although my parents would never have considered my attending medical school, they valued education highly and always encouraged studying hard." She added during the interview, "I get the feeling that they are very proud of me now—especially my dad—although he would have probably preferred my brothers to become doctors. However, my brothers were not interested in studying for so many more years."

A few days before classes were to begin at UCSF, at a reception for recipients of Regents Scholarships, Tomoko met Richard (Rich) Hooper.

Though by ancestry from diverse backgrounds, they had a common history in having parents whose lives were marked by World War II. Rich's father, William (Jerry) Hooper, an experienced pilot in the Royal New Zealand Air Force (RNZAF), fought in the Battle of Britain and throughout the Blitz as a flight instructor and combat pilot.[9] During those harrowing years, he found time to court and marry his secretary, an ebullient daughter of a Scottish Highland minister with flaming red hair. Rich, their first son, was born in 1943. In 1947, Rich's father took his young family and returned to New Zealand. There he joined other ex-RNZAF pilots in the new business of aerial topdressing, a method of aerial application of fertilizer and seed by planes for erosion control and soil enhancement in New Zealand's mountains and remote farmlands. After surviving the perils of air combat during the war, Jerry Hooper's luck ran out. He became New Zealand's first casualty of aerial topdressing in October of 1950. With insufficient air speed to complete a climbing turn after a sowing run, he and his DH82 Tiger Moth crashed into a mountainside.[10]

Almost a decade after that tragic accident and with the encouragement of close friends who had moved to the San Francisco Bay Area, Rich's mother immigrated to the US with her sons. They settled in Sunnyvale, California. After completing high school, Rich enrolled in Foothill College in Los Altos Hills near Mountain View for two years, then transferred to UC Berkeley in preparation for application to medical school. After graduation, he took a year off to hitchhike across the US and back again. He wanted to explore his new country and see who lived in it before becoming a naturalized citizen.

From their first meeting, Tomoko and Rich's lives became linked— initially, quite literally, by a cadaver. The alphabetical proximity of H and I brought Rich Hooper and Tomoko Inadomi together as partners for gross anatomy. With two other classmates, they shared a cadaver. They studied together for exams. Within six months, they announced their engagement and married just before the start of the second year of classes. It proved to be a very happy union for both. Such are the ways of romance in medical school.

Although Tomoko selected medical school over her other choices, she cited none of the motivations for a medical career common to most of the women in the group. She had no early interest in medicine or science, no encouragement from family or friends, no brush with illness or death, no missionary desire to help or heal. Her story sounded as though some reluctant but gravitational inevitability pulled her toward medicine. She described herself as ambitious and a perfectionist but unconfident. "My husband tells me I have an inferiority complex," she told Lillian.

During their fourth year at UCSF, Tomoko and Rich received a Lange Fellowship from Jack Lange and his medical textbook publishing company to work at the Methodist-sponsored Christ Hospital in Kapit, Sarawak, Borneo.[11] Established in 1957 by Dr. Bu Tien Siew, a physician from New York, the hospital clung to the edge of the tropical forest at the basin of the Rajang River. Rich and Tomoko's experience of witnessing medical care accessible only by long, jungle-river journeys for often preventable diseases and injuries left a lasting impression on them. They, too, traveled the muddy rivers and tried not to think about snakes and other jungle dangers involved with bringing care to isolated communities. Tomoko vividly remembered infants with neonatal tetanus from the local practice of rubbing river mud on the umbilical cord of newborns to stop bleeding. The Borneo experience stimulated their interest in public health and patterns of disease occurrence and prevention.

After graduating from UCSF and completing rotating internships at Sacramento Medical Center, an affiliate of UC Davis School of Medicine, Tomoko and Rich moved to Hawaii. Knowing that military service would be in his future, Rich had previously joined the US Naval Reserves while in medical school. In Honolulu, he did a Preventive Medicine residency at the

University of Hawaii in conjunction with his Naval commitment through the Berry Plan, and then became an active duty Naval officer in Preventive Medicine, a professional choice he retained throughout his career. Tomoko earned a Master of Public Health (MPH) in Family Planning at the University of Hawaii in 1973 while Rich was stationed at Pearl Harbor. She then developed teaching aids for nurse practitioners in family planning clinics at the University of Hawaii and at a community hospital in Honolulu. With a subsequent move to California, she collaborated with a faculty member at the University of Southern California to develop further teaching materials for nurse practitioners in family planning, as well as working part-time at a community health center in San Ysidro near the Mexican border. After moving back to the San Francisco Bay Area, she worked part-time in the emergency room at Kaiser Hospital in Walnut Creek.

Throughout her early years of marriage and medicine, Tomoko wanted a family. In many ways, it was her primary desire. Even while in medical school, she told Lillian, "I only wanted to practice medicine for a limited number of hours, and I always wanted to combine work and family."

In 1973, with the efficiency of having fraternal twins, her wish for a family materialized. She and her husband became parents of a son and a daughter. In the 1975 interview, Tomoko told Lillian, "I never thought about not having children. I always thought I would do it regardless of career goals. I enjoyed my pregnancy—I was so cheerful and elated to be pregnant with twins. I was sick for only one week." After her children were born, with her husband in the Navy and the necessity of moving every three to four years, she wanted to stay home and raise the twins. Though she did not dismiss working part-time at some point, when asked about her plans for the next five years, she said, "I like crafts and want to take courses in ceramics. I want to develop a good marriage and be a good mother. I am less ambitious and less energetic than younger mothers. I have come to realize that I have some limits and must make compromises."

When Lillian again met with Tomoko in 1990, it was clear that she had accomplished her goal of being a successful mother. She described herself as a "super-mom" to her sixteen-year-old son and daughter. Her many child-oriented activities included volunteering at their schools, supporting her daughter's interest in gymnastics, working with the Boy Scouts of America as advancement chairperson, and writing a manual for parents with children in Scouting. Tomoko's previous experiences in developing teaching materials for nurse practitioners in family planning and her strong writing skills proved valuable in her work with the Boy Scouts. In fact, her writing and editing skills, in addition to her medical background, were of even greater value to her husband, Rich. Throughout her years of child-rearing, she actively participated in his work by assisting him in numerous projects related to military medicine and, in particular, the health of Naval personnel. For example, Tomoko helped to write Rich's 1993 publication, "US Hospital Ships: A Proposal for Their Use in Humanitarian Missions," an article that advocated for the ships, the *Mercy* and the *Comfort*, to be symbols of international compassion.[12] Rich wanted to add Tomoko's name on the JAMA article as co-author, but she declined.

Tomoko minimized her professional contributions. In 1990 she told Lillian, "My medical career has disappeared into nothingness, but it is the life I want. I have always considered raising my children as my primary objective. I would not change anything."

Then, in 1992, life changed—drastically. Tomoko and Rich were living in Vienna, Virginia, for his assignment at the Uniformed Services University of Health Sciences (USUHS) in Bethesda, Maryland.[13] In the same month as they discussed a trip to England and Scotland to celebrate their twenty-fifth wedding anniversary, Rich received the devastating news that he had colon cancer with liver metastases. Though they continued with their planned trip at Rich's insistence, they returned to face two and a half years of chemotherapy regimens for Rich. He died in 1994 at the age of fifty-one.

It was during the difficult years of Rich's illness that Tomoko, with Rich's encouragement, enrolled at USUHS to earn her second MPH degree in order to refresh her knowledge of preventive medicine and public health. At the age of fifty, with the circumstances and financial basis of her life totally altered and her children away from home in college, Tomoko reentered medicine.

Initially she worked part-time at USUHS as a research assistant on a study that Rich had undertaken on the health implications of extended undersea deployment of US Navy submarine crew members. The isolation and contained environment of life aboard submarines also had possible implications for predicting health risks for astronauts on extended space missions. Over the next four years, Tomoko additionally worked on other studies relevant to the health of military personnel.

In 1999, Tomoko joined the USUHS as a full-time faculty member. With this position and its added independence, she tackled epidemiological studies with prodigious energy and her own perspective. Her career took off.

She and her colleague at USUHS, Gary D. Gackstetter, DVM, MPH, PhD, embarked on a large study in conjunction with the Naval Health Research Center (NHRC) in San Diego, CA, to answer the question: *does serving in the military affect any health outcomes?* The project, known as the Millennium Cohort Study and sponsored by the Department of Defense, followed 200,000 service men and women from all military branches in a longitudinal evaluation of comprehensive health-related parameters, including psychological as well as physical outcomes. The health of veterans of the 1991 Gulf War was of particular interest in the early epidemiological studies. When Lillian contacted her for this fifty-year follow-up, she was working fifty to sixty hours per week, down from her eighty hours per week during the previous thirteen years while she built up her teaching, research,

Tomoko Hooper, photo at her retirement, courtesy of Tomoko Hooper

and service portfolios.

While she started with research on submarine crew members, Tomoko eventually collaborated on social-behavioral studies, including the health effects of sexual harassment and smoking. She ended her academic career as a full Professor in the Department of Preventive Medicine and Biometrics at the Uniformed Services University. Here she taught, supervised an administrative staff, and engaged with public health practitioners in the field to serve as research mentors and practicum preceptors to her graduate students. In 2010, she was elected President of the Faculty Senate, the first female to hold that title. In 2013, she received the Outstanding Biomedical

Graduate Educator Award. Upon her retirement in July of 2019, the Dean of the School of Medicine appointed her Professor Emerita and commended her outstanding work throughout her twenty-five-year career.

In our interview, I asked Norma how she made her decisions. She replied that she did what made sense for her at each particular time. She had her eye on the future, but also an eye on the present, and she had patience. The right time to take a break was 1972—to reflect on her father's life and mourn his recent death, to relax and earn some funds, and, as it turned out, to reconnect with Jim Schmitt. A few years later, it was the right time to begin a family. And then, most definitely, 1983 was the right time to launch her career in earnest which then sped along to great success and fulfillment for the next twenty-six years. One telling detail that foretold the future was there all along. When Norma married Jim, she functioned as Mrs. Schmitt. But actually, quietly, she remained Dr. McKenzie. Norma knew who she was.

The hand of fate played a more active role in Tomoko's life. Without question, she more than fulfilled her primary desire to be a good wife and mother. In the background and evidenced by her subsequent career, she must have paid close attention to her husband's career in the Navy and shared his interest in epidemiology and environmental factors impinging on health. When the combination of tragedy and financial necessity altered her life, Tomoko transformed herself. She had earlier described herself as "ambitious and a perfectionist but unconfident." In the end, ambition and perfectionism claimed victory.

PART III

Funding from the Robert Wood Johnson Foundation allowed Lillian to undertake follow-up studies on the women in her original group—the Time 2 study in 1975 and the Time 3 study in 1990.[1] These follow-ups sealed the project as historic, especially so since the participation of the cohort remained high. At Time 3, fifty-three of the fifty-seven surviving women filled out a questionnaire and completed multiple personality tests. Lillian met with forty-nine of the women for a third, in-depth interview. She summarized the study for the Foundation. From the twenty-five-year perspective, she identified how life unfolded for two groups of women who faced similar situations. First, she looked at the fifteen women whose children had various problems or disabilities. Second, she identified the women who had particularly harmonious lives by all objective measurements. In addition, she described the whole group's personality in midlife.

CHAPTER 8

CHALLENGING CHILDREN

By 1990, 83% of the women were mothers. And for most of the women, the stressful years of juggling career with the demands of a young family had receded into the past. Their children were in the later years of elementary school or high school and had gained degrees of independence. Many of the children were well on their way to display the successful academic and leadership qualities that were to follow them into adulthood.

Nancy Doyle, however, was not alone in facing the burden of caring for a child with multiple physical and emotional problems. Fifteen women had children who presented challenges. The type and complexity of these challenges varied, ranging from minor and solvable to life-long problems that defied simple solutions. Lillian reported that it was obvious that the women who faced these difficulties loved their children. And many deployed a highly successful array of skills to help their children. Yet, invariably, the children altered their mothers' lives and, at least in the years around midlife career, added a burden. For privacy, many of these women will not be named.

Helene Olson's older son had no motivation in school between the ages of eleven and thirteen. Failing grades filled his report card. Then Helene took him in hand. She set aside extra time to help him with his school work. Her husband remained, as always, supportive and nurturing to his son. Almost overnight, he changed. Both his grades and attitude toward school improved. This added dose of understanding and positive effort helped him over the hump.

Other problems were situational and could involve the entire family.

The young-adult daughter of one of the women, Dr. X, survived a natural disaster in which she was one of only two survivors of an accident that killed eleven of her friends. The tragedy affected the whole family with feelings of survivor guilt and PTSD for which they sought therapy. In the aftermath, Dr. X found emotional support from her female friends rather than from her husband. In her comment to Lillian, she said, that in the end, "I found a better sense of who I am, a more spiritual awareness of myself. It's given me a greater desire to be useful to others. I want my life to matter. I am a peaceful human being. I want to be useful to the community." In helping her daughter through the tragedy, Dr. X accessed her full reserve of resiliency. Almost paradoxically, her son, who was not involved in the accident, continued to suffer and required treatment for depression for many years.

For a parent caring for a child with emotional or physical problems, suicide of the child is an overwhelming tragedy. One physician faced this heartbreaking outcome. The suicide led the physician to elect an early retirement. She faulted herself that she had not taken more time off when her children were young.

Some of the women found remarkable strength and agency in helping their children in ways that redefined who they were.

Dr. Y had always wanted a family in addition to a career and decided to do things in sequence. First, she finished a rigorous residency. When offered a faculty position in her specialty, she shared with the department chief that she would want to work part-time when she became pregnant. The chief assured her that he would honor this request as a precondition for employment. However, when she did become pregnant, he reneged on the agreement. If she didn't continue to work full-time, he said, she would have to resign.

Dr. Y continued to work full-time. At twenty-two weeks gestation, she suffered a miscarriage. She never forgave the department chief's cavalier dismissal of his promise to her. Whether he forgot or not, such was the prevailing culture of medicine in the 1970s—and beyond. Dr. Y subsequently gave birth to a son. Although premature, he grew and developed without problems. The situation was not so fortunate with her next child, a daughter.

At her premature birth, her daughter weighed two pounds. It soon became obvious that she had cerebral palsy with motor and cognitive deficits. With that early realization, Dr. Y's life changed forever. She and her husband enveloped their daughter in a web of love and support without bounds. Though her daughter has visual and motor impairments, her achievements have been remarkable. She participated in all of the family activities and even in the Special Olympics. As a young adult, she gained enough independence to live in a group home. To this day, Dr. Y visits her frequently and talks with her daily.

In their interview in 1990, Lillian noted, "The striking thing is how grateful Dr. Y is about the quality of her life even though she has a severely disabled daughter. She loves her daughter's smile." And Dr. Y told Lillian, "She has changed me so I am no longer a perfectionist." In each conversation, what would shine through was Dr. Y's intense bond of love for her daughter.

For the other nine women, their children had various degrees of neurodevelopmental disorders. Today, the diagnoses would center on Attention Deficit Hyperactivity Disorder or Autism Spectrum Disorder. But, in the 1980s and '90s, these syndromes were poorly recognized and defined. Even today, the labels cover a wide spectrum of learning, communication, and behavioral disorders that are incompletely understood. Genetics, possible environmental exposures, and nongenetic factors are all likely involved.

In the interviews, some of the women reported that they found the challenge a humbling experience and, at times, wanted to quit work and stay home with their child. In one way or another, though, everyone managed.

Sarita Eastman and son Ian, 1978, courtesy of Sarita Eastman

In particular, Sarita Eastman, the eldest girl of nine siblings, the daughter of a surgeon mother and pediatrician father, rose to the challenge. She took charge.

Sarita's younger son had severe problems with impulse control. When Lillian interviewed her in 1990, they met at Sarita's home. As they talked in the kitchen, her son climbed to the top of the refrigerator with the family cat tucked under one arm. He then held the poor feline aloft and wanted to hurl it into space. It was a Roald Dahl-moment that occurred often in the Eastman household. Though somewhat stymied, Sarita remained unusually calm. She was becoming an expert in this sort of behavior.

She had trained as a pediatrician at UCSF and practiced general pediatrics in San Diego. Beginning in the late 1970s with her growing awareness of her son's disorder, she set about learning how best to help him. She said, "That led to my becoming a self-taught specialist among my colleagues who began sending me all their patients with similar problems" of behavior and difficulty in school and social settings.

Sarita was also a woman of action. She developed a wide network of healthcare professionals, educators, and parents concerned with children who fell into this "learning-different" area and became well-known in the community for her expertise. In 1988, she and a group of other visionaries founded The Winston School for Children with Learning Differences in Del Mar, CA. Encompassing the elementary grades through high school, the school was the first of its kind in Southern California. When subspecialty boards became established, Sarita earned certification by the Board of Developmental-Behavioral Pediatrics in 1999. Thereafter, she devoted her practice exclusively to that subspecialty, to great demand and her professional pleasure. When she retired in 2012, Sarita said those final years of her career were the most rewarding.

CHAPTER 9

THE FOUR ACES

At the twenty-five year milestone in 1990, the study also identified a group of seven women for whom personal life and professional career had worked out exceptionally well. These women rated themselves "very high" on Specialty Fit, Career Satisfaction, Role Harmony, and Overall Life Satisfaction. Gamblers or not, they ended up holding "four aces."

The women found themselves in this enviable group in mid-career at an average age of forty-six. Their specialty choices covered the medical spectrum with three women in internal medicine and one each in dermatology, radiology, nuclear medicine, and pediatrics. Two had academic careers and five were in private practice, two of whom worked as solo practitioners of their specialties. All of the women had board certification in their primary specialty and several had additional boards in subspecialty areas. One "super-acer" earned board certification in internal medicine, endocrinology, and nuclear medicine. Without question, these women had deep commitments to their careers.

Of note, none of the women were employed by an HMO. Each woman within the group had been able to achieve considerable independence in defining the direction of her career.

Three of the women, Faith, Rima, and Sarita, described in this manuscript, are examples. By 1990, Faith stood high in the pantheon of legendary clinicians and teachers. Rima, in her quiet and modest way, had earned a national and international reputation in toxoplasmosis research. As one of the leading pediatric authorities on behavioral issues of children, Sarita was preeminent throughout Southern California for her work in the education of children with special needs.

Five women were married to their first and only husband. None of these five women experienced divorce—as verified in the now-completed fifty-year follow-up. Four of the husbands were physicians. The five married women all had children, on average two. By the time of the final follow-up, all of the children were doing well. And, of paramount importance, all five women reported that their husbands were supportive of their careers and helped with the children.

The "four aces" who married were also similar in that they were born in the US into families deemed high socioeconomic status by the parameters of this study. Their fathers had prosperous jobs—four were physicians and one was an engineer. For one woman, both parents were physicians. They all had childhoods without hardship in stable, two-parent homes without divorces.

Two women neither married nor had a partner and remained childless. They were single by choice and did not wish to divide their time between their profession and family. Both women had many friends and interests. Faith characterized her decision well. Singularly directed to medicine and teaching, she found fulfillment in life within this orbit. As Lillian said, "Medicine was her lust. Indeed, it was her life." In a sense, her students were her progeny and legacy. Photographs of Faith with her students and colleagues lined her office and verified at a glance her joy in her chosen career. Even her aged dogs found a place. She chose the life she loved.

In summary, the women in this group of seven mostly came from stable backgrounds with adequate financial means. If they married, they had children. Moreover, their husbands shared their educational attainments, employment status, and family-life values.

As Lillian stated in her report to the Robert Wood Johnson Foundation, "All in all, they share the blessings of good fortune. The place of the luck-of-the-draw is unmeasured and usually not given much attention in the studies of adult development. Fate is hard to quantify; we live in a society which places the burden of responsibility for fortune—good and bad—upon the individual. But an unlucky pregnancy resulting in a child with severe birth defects colors a life in many ways, as does having breast cancer or fertility problems. As a result, the quest is for different things, one tries to find answers to different questions, and one learns how to play out a 'bad hand' with grace as do many who do not hold four aces."

In 1990, she said, "The spirit of the entire group, despite holding some 'bad cards,' is very high. The overall life satisfaction rating is excellent with 92% saying that their life, taken as a whole, is satisfying or very satisfying."

CHAPTER 10

ARC OF CAREERS

Lillian and her colleague, Paul Wink, evaluated personality changes over time within the group.[1] The results of two standard psychological and personality tests, the California Psychological Inventory and the Adjective Check List, taken by the women at each of the three time intervals, formed the basis of the analysis. As part of a twenty-five-year longitudinal study, the conclusions permitted a rare view of how a selected group of female physicians changed with time.

On one level, the results documented how much the women stayed the same. Compared to other women studied, such as mathematicians, psychologists, or Mills College women, they started and remained significantly higher than other groups in Achievement via Independence, Tolerance, and Psychological Mindedness and lower than others on Femininity.

As Lillian wrote, "This enduring pattern is the container and context for viewing all subsequent change. Consideration of these scores connotes an extremely competent, independent, intellectually superior group of women. They have high aspirations and can work independently, flexibly, and creatively to achieve their goals. They will be seen by others as insightful, imaginative, logical, verbally fluent, and autonomous." Their interest in science, considered a less feminine attribute on the tests, continued.

There were some subtle changes. As a whole, the group experienced a steady improvement in ability to perform and achieve in highly structured situations that required adherence to agreed-on ways of accomplishing tasks. The Achievement via Conformance scores documented this change.

Medicine is a team sport. It requires a physician to work within a system, be the system an HMO, academic institution, hospital, private group, multi-specialty clinic, research institution, or any of a myriad of other ways one uses medical training. To work with colleagues and institutions, adaptation and discipline are required. Teamwork with colleagues can additionally be one of the great pleasures of the profession. On the whole, to function as a mature professional in medicine would require adjustment to elements of a structured environment. The spunky individuality of some of the women at Time 1 had become muted by Time 3—perhaps the only personality-related casualty.

At the twenty-five-year mark, the tests also documented an increase in scores on Responsibility, Self-Control, and Good Impression reflecting that the women had become more dominant, responsible, and self-controlled. These are changes that go hand in hand with advancement of their careers into more prestigious positions within medicine and within their communities. Their expertise had become more widely recognized and valued. Lillian noted that similar changes were identified in longitudinal studies of women in other professions, but with women physicians, the changes emerged earlier in their career.

This fifty-year follow-up, basically a Time 4, offers some statistics relevant to career satisfaction. At Time 2 in 1976, 88% of women reported high career satisfaction. The rating dipped to 79% in 1990 at the mid-career point. But by Time 4 in 2017, the rating rebounded with 94% of women reporting high career satisfaction. Only 6% had average satisfaction and no one reported disappointment. Considering how much of one's life is spent working, this degree of career fulfillment and gratification is noteworthy. We chose our profession well.

The mean length of their careers underscored their dedication and satisfaction. In 2017, twenty-four women (65%) were fully retired, the majority having retired between 2005-2017. Impressively, the average retiree spent approximately forty years working after graduation from UCSF. The main reason cited for retiring was that "the time was right." Poor health of herself or a family member entered into the decision for some. A few mentioned that the growing bureaucracy in their medical setting was implicated in their decision to retire as well as the cost of malpractice insurance. Thirteen women were still working either part-time (19%) or full-time (16%).

Their collective opinions about medicine today were revealing. Virtually every woman mentioned the great technological changes in diagnosis and treatment of diseases and the huge advancements in science basic to medicine. From the point of scientific knowledge, their time in medical school constituted a different era from that of their retirement. The group remained very positive about the greater ethnic diversity within medicine and applauded the greater numbers of women at all levels of the medical hierarchy. The diminution in time spent with patients stood as the most cited professional problem, largely due to the concomitant intrusion of the electronic medical record in their practice situations.

I have always thought that the years of my career spanned the golden age of American medicine. The large, multispecialty clinic and hospital in which I practiced was run by physicians and functioned with the spirit of a partnership. Indeed, it was an actual partnership of physicians when I first joined Virginia Mason in 1980 and became its first female partner three years later. An assessment of what was best for the patient guided nearly every institutional decision. Other parameters, including finances, assumed a secondary status. As an institution, we were fortunate to be able to participate in the major and groundbreaking advancements in diagnosis, treatment, and the underlying science of medicine that occurred at rapid speed. Yet gradually, as the decades passed, the organization became more corporate. The administrative voice of the nonphysician grew louder. Financial considerations loomed larger. The "white coats versus the suits" became the vernacular in discussions of institutional priorities. The chief financial officer referred to physicians as RGUs, revenue-generating units, behind our backs. The electronic medical record, primarily aimed at capturing billing information, assumed dominance over disease description. As I watched this slow transformation, I realized how fortunate I had been to have experienced the majority of my career in the earlier years—especially before the turn of the century.

In the fifty-year assessment material returned by participants, a section asked for self-rating about satisfaction with career in medicine and life in general. Twenty-five of the women completed this section. On the question, "How good a fit was your career in medicine with your talents and needs?" 94% of the physicians responded that the fit was excellent or very good; two women believed the fit was average. On the question of "I am satisfied with my life," 96% agreed. The most remarkable agreement of 100% came with the question "So far I have gotten the important things I want in life." This broad question covered everything in their lives—marriages, children, financial state, profession—and correlated very well with their assessment of their professional career. Our timing in medicine had been excellent.

CHAPTER 11

DINOSAURS OR VANGUARD

It took 100 years to go from zero to ten. The Toland Medical College, founded in 1864, admitted no women. By the time of this study of the entering classes from 1964 to 1967, 10% of UCSF medical students were women, a number above the national average of 8%. Within the next fifty years, women skyrocketed to be 52% of the class of 2020.

Dr. Toland gifted his medical college to the Medical Department of the new University of California at Berkeley in 1873. Lucy Maria Field Wanzer applied almost immediately only to have her application summarily rejected by the school based solely on her gender.[1] On her behalf, two Regents of the University and their attorneys demanded review of her case. As the Medical Department was deemed an integral part of the University, and the Charter for the University provided for access to education by both sexes, Lucy Wanzer gained admission based on her excellent credentials. Her rejection "on the basis of sex" was overturned. With the matriculation of Wanzer, females instantly zoomed to be 5% of the twenty medical students that composed the class of 1876.

Despite the Regents' decision, the Dean of the Medical Department remained disgruntled. He encouraged Wanzer's fellow students to haze her to force her resignation. His plan failed miserably. Her fellow students came to accept, and ultimately to admire, her. Yet the faculty placed hurdles in her path. Though he welcomed her, Dr. Hugh Toland, then Professor of Diseases, felt it would be too strenuous (his word) if she accompanied him to the syphilitic and gonorrheal ward. Wanzer replied, "Oh yes, doctor; I know the work is hard, but I want to see everything, otherwise I would not be fit to be a medical student." The attending physician for eye diseases told her a woman had no business to study medicine. If she did, she ought to have her ovaries removed. Wanzer replied that "if this were so, the men students ought to have their testicles removed." Dr. Beverly Cole, who led the obstetrical clinic, meant well when he told her that he would not like to place her in an unpleasant position, but he could not lecture to a mixed class without making it very embarrassing to her. He thought it best to excuse her from the course. Wanzer countered that she wished to be excused from nothing. Pleased by her pluck, Cole offered to be her preceptor.

The road with her fellow students was also not without bumps. One morning when she came to the dissecting room to explore a hernia repair on her cadaver, an unusual number of students loitered nearby. "Her cadaver had been rearranged in a manner that they thought would shock her very much. She took no notice of it and went on working as if nothing had happened." Alas, the sense of humor of male medical students evolved little over the next century. On another morning decades later in 1968, Schumarry found a penis added to the pelvis of the female cadaver she shared with three giggling cadaver-comrades as she withdrew the covering sheet. One can imagine this scene unfolding on a near-yearly basis.

Wanzer graduated in November of the Centennial year, 1876. Dr. Cole, by now her admirer as well as preceptor, presented her name for admittance to the San Francisco County Medical Society. Some members threatened to blackball her nomination and suggested she withdraw. Her reply: "My name stands; blackball me if you will." Her name stood. She became the first female member of the Society.

Wanzer went on to have a markedly successful career devoted predominantly to the health and welfare of women and children. Notably she was one of the founders of the San Francisco Children's Hospital. Though she had been married briefly as a young woman, she divorced seven years prior to medical school and neither remarried nor had children. Confusion surrounding the newness of the idea of a female doctor, however, popped up here and there. In written articles about her and minutes of meetings, uncertainty revealed itself in references to Doctress Wanzer or Mrs. Dr. Wanzer. Regardless of how her name was communicated, Dr. Wanzer received heaps of accolades, recognition, and honors throughout her long career which lasted well into her eighties. Women entering medicine in San Francisco found in her a willing mentor and proponent. In an article from the *San Francisco Chronicle*, 13 October 1921, titled "Dr. Lucy Wanzer, Age 80, Tells of Love for Work and Happy Life," she "says her life has been happy and tells us that the secret of happiness is a love for our chosen profession. She loves the work of healing the sick."

Wanzer would have fit well with the UCSF women of the 1960s. She was the firstborn to parents who prized education, and she received a good education in Milwaukee, Wisconsin, and Hartford, Connecticut. She assumed major family responsibilities by age eleven, primarily in caring for her mother who suffered from what was then called lung fever (tuberculosis). This early exposure to health care likely set her on her path to medical school. The family moved to California because of her mother's poor health when Wanzer was seventeen. From then on, she worked as a teacher in Alameda County, as a dressmaker, and in a postmaster position to help support her family and save money in preparation for studying medicine. She fit our demographics: a family that valued education for daughters, an early focus on medicine, and an independent, industrious worker.

However, another perspective is the reverse. Would we, the fifty-eight women in this study, fit into the UCSF class of 1876? Our sights were set on medicine from an early age, our parents encouraged education, most of us were the first or second born, and many of us had to earn our own funds to finance medical school. Gaining admittance to medical school was only the first barrier to surmount. Once a fully fledged physician, breaking into a professional practice was arguably even harder.

Though Wanzer immediately opened an office on Geary Street, her practice got off to a slow start despite promises of help from her friends. "But very few sent other than their servant girls. At first she had to practice among the very poorest persons from Tar Flat (a poor neighborhood south of Market Street in an area contaminated by layers of toxic tar sludge from the industrial distillation of coal). Gradually she got a better class. When the mistresses found their servant girls did not die, they came themselves."

We, too, faced discrimination. Bonnie worked for free in order to break into oncology in Boise; Nancy's salary in her pediatric practice was less per hour than that of the office staff; the head of pathology in Everett, Washington, declared that if he hired me, he would not pay me. Like Wanzer, many of us had to fight our way into careers in a male-dominated profession skeptical of female physicians and devoid of mentors. Still, like the indomitable Dr. Lucy Wanzer, we persevered, in many ways triumphed, and loved our chosen profession.

Lillian labeled us as "pioneer women physicians." My perspective is that we arrived at an inflection point for women in medicine, perhaps more as the last of the dinosaurs than the vanguard of the future. As the tail end of the Silent Generation, we missed being Boomers. Instead, we inhabited a generational no-man's-land where we chose to be doctors because we liked science, wanted to use our intellect, had confidence, and possessed a general desire to help people. Though feminist literature existed, feminism was far from a widespread movement until the early 1970s. By then, we were over the barricade. Most of us were too busy in residency or early practice to notice that a fight was on. But, in the end, *pioneer* may be the best descriptor.[2] The root word in English is a military term from the French, *peonaris*, a foot soldier who, with pick and shovel, clears the ground before an advancing army and digs the trenches before the battle.[3] For us, women physicians entering medicine in the '60s, no later metaphorical interpretation of pioneer is needed. We shoveled our way into the profession, knew where to find the trenches, and prepared the terrain for the main body of troops.

Now, almost 150 years after Dr. Lucy Wanzer began her career, nearly every woman in this group counts becoming a physician one of the best, if not the absolute best, decision of her life.

ENDNOTES

Chapter 1

1. Cartwright. Conscious Factors Entering into Decisions of Women to Study Medicine. *Journal of Social Issues.* 1972; 28(3);   201-215.

2. Lillian Cartwright in conversation with author.

3. Lillian Kaufman Cartwright, *Women in Medical School.* Dissertation. Graduate Division of the University of California, Berkeley. 1970. (unpublished)

4. Cartwright, Wink, Kmetz. What Leads to Good Health in Midlife Women Physicians? Some Clues From a Longitudinal Study. *Psychosomatic Medicine* 1995; 57:284-292. Cartwright, Adams, Ostrove, Stewart, Wink. Psychological Predictors of Good Health in Three Longitudinal Samples of Educated Midlife Women. *Health Psychology* 1998; 17(5):412-420.

5. Cartwright, Wink. Personality Change in Women Physicians from Medical Student Years to Mid-40s. *Psychology of Women Quarterly* 1994; 18:291-308.

6. IRB approval: letter from Margaret Keane, IRB Psychology Department Subcommittee Wellesley College, May 31, 2017, approved Wellesley College IRB, under 46.110(b)(1).

Chapter 2

1. 1868-1898 The Origins of the University of California and Affiliated Colleges. history.library.ucsf.edu. Retrieved 2020-06-26.

2. Saint Louis University School of Medicine. wikipedia. Retrieved 2020-06-26.

3. 1868-1898 The Origins of the University of California and Affiliated Colleges. history.library.ucsf.edu.

4. Cartwright. Personality Differences in Male and Female Medical Students. *Psychiatry in Medicine* 1972; 3:213-218.

5. Ibid.

6. Cartwright. The Personality and Family Background of a Sample of Women Medical Students at the University of California; *Journal of the American Medical Association* 1972; 27(5):260-266.

Chapter 3

1. Bemelmans, Ludwig. *Madeline*. Viking Press, 1951. ISBN 0670445800.

2. Alsace-Lorraine. Shoah Resource Center. www.yadvashem.org/odot_pdf/%20 word%20-%205729.pdf.

3. www.military museum.org/Letterman.

4. www.civilwarmed.org/letterman and rand.org/Providing for the Casualties of War www.battlefields.org/learn/biographies/jonathan_letterman.

5. npshistory.com/publications SSSI Letterman-NPS History.

6. Chandler, Lila. *Mission. Medical. Witness. The Stories of Southwestern Medical Clinic*. Ch. 10. The Birth Place, pp. 82-88. 2013. published by Southwestern Medical Clinic Foundation. ISBN 978-0-9899708-0-8.

7. Ibid. p. 82.

8. Ibid. p. 85.

9. Ibid. p. 83.

10. Ibid. pp. 83-84.

11. 2019 autobiography, UCSF Archives.

12. Ibid.

13. Cartwright, Wink, Kmetz. What Leads to Good Health in Midlife Women Physicians? Some Clues From a Longitudinal Study. *Psychosomatic Medicine* 1995; 57:284-292.

14. Tule Lake Relocation Center information from encyclopedia.densho.org/Tule_ Lake/.

15. Information: www.encyclopedia.densho.org/_(Granada)/ and nps.gov/places/ granada-relocation-center.htm. See also: www.pbs.org/colorado-experience-am-ache/ and http://amache.org/overview/ and www.cogreatwomen.org/project/ amache-prowers/.

16. Topaz War Relocation Center information from encyclopedia.densho.org/ Topaz/, Topaz Museum (topazmuseum.org) and www.nps.gov/places/central-utah-relocation-site.

17. Information on Obata from encyclopedia.densho.org/Chiura_Obata/ and from the Smithsonian Institution sites: Chiura Obata: American Modern. Smithsonian American Art Museum 7/1/20 and Chiura Obata's by Prof. ShiPu Wang. smithsonianmag.com/smithsonian-institution/how-japanese-artist-chiura-obata-be-american-great-1880974070. Additional information from Wood, Cirrus. Artist Interned: A Berkeley Legend Beauty in "Enormous Bleakness" of War Camp. alumni.berkeley.edu/california-magazine/just-in/2017-04-25/.

Chapter 4

1. sciencedaily.com/releases/1999/02/990222072704.htm Investigation solves Final Mystery of Ishi. The Last of the Yahi Indians.

2. Cartwright, LK. "Medicine Is My Lust: The Story of a Woman Physician." In *Women Creating Lives*, edited by Carol E. Franz and Abigail J. Stewart, 1994, Westview Press, Boulder, SF. Oxford, pp.201-212.

3. arthur-conan-doyle.com/index.php?title_Bell and www.uwpress.wisc.edu, Liebow, EM. Dr. Joe Bell.Model for Sherlock Holmes.

4. Cartwright. Medicine is My Lust, p. 208.

5. Ibid. p. 208.

6. Ibid. p. 209.

7. Ibid. p. 209.

8. Ibid. pp. 209-210.

9. youtube.com/watch?v=fbB8PeMatZo.

10. Peabody FW. Landmark article March 9, 1927: The care of the patient. By Francis W. Peabody. JAMA 1984;252(6):813-8.

11. Medical Super Sleuth stories.ucdavis.edu/stories/faculty/fitzgerald.

12. Fitzgerald, FT. Curiosity. On Being a Doctor. *Annals of Internal Medicine* 1999; 130(1), 70-72.

13. www.youtube.com/watch?v=fbB8PeMatZ0 Last Lecture Series, Gold Humanism Honor Society.

14. youtube.com/watch?v=VNbbKGGvMrk Daboise on East 8.

15. Crawford, F. Medical experts and scholars, including Cornell professor, rule out foul play in death of Wolfgang Amadeus Mozart. news.cornell.edu/stories/2000/02/foul-play-ruled-out-death-wolfgang-amadeus-mozart.

16. blubrry.com S2E9 The Stories We Tell.

17. *We Were Fellows*. Self-published book, copyright held by Jack Remington and James Krahenbuhl, 2009, pp. 160-172.

18. Berry, FB. The Story of "The Berry Plan." *Bull NY Acad Med*; 1976; 52(3) 278-282.

19. https://history.amedd.army.mil/boosddocs/wwii/actusurgconvoli/CH18.htm U.S. Army Medical Department Office of Medical History, Chapter XVIII, pp.505-515.

20. Berry, FB. The Story of "The Berry Plan." *Bull NY Acad Med* 1976; 52(3), p.280.

21. *We Were Fellows*, p. 164.

22. Ibid., p. 165.

23. Ibid., p. 167.

24. Cartwright LK. Career Satisfaction and Role Harmony in a Sample of Young Women Physicians. *Journal of Vocational Behavior* 1978; 12:184-196.

Chapter 5

1. Cartwright LK. Career Satisfaction and Role Harmony in a Sample of Young Women Physicians. *Journal of Vocational Behavior* 1978; 12:184-196; Cartwright LK. Occupational Stress in Women Physicians. 1987; *Stress in Health Professionals*, Edited by R. Payne and J. Firth-Cozens, John Wiley and Sons Ltd, 71-87.

2. Angeles Arrien: Walking the Mystical Path with Practical Feet. www.angelesarrien.com and The Legacy of Angeles Arrien. www.charterforcompassion.org.

3. Christine Page MD. christinepage.com/about-christine-page-md/.

4. www.faim.org/international-society-for-the-studies-of-subtle-energies-and-energy-medicine.

5. Author of *Souls on Earth: Exploring Interplanetary Past Lives* and other books.

6. www.history.state.gov/milesstones/1937-1945/chinese-excluion-act-repeal.

7. www.washingtonpost.com/news/made-by-history/wp/2017/08/06/the-1984-olympics.

Chapter 6

1. The Bellevue Leader (Offutt AFB, Bellevue, Nebraska) Dec 7, 1988.

2. The Midway Atoll You Might Not Know. www.fws.gov/refuges/features/.

3. www.ncbi.nih.gov/pmc/articles/ PMC3178858/.

4. ncbi.nih.gov/pmc/articles/PMC4953321/2100 Jun;11(3):261-264 (madness, not due to porphyria but probable bipolar disorder and dementia).

5. The Gold-Headed Cane by William Macmichael-Project Gutenberg. www.gutenberg.org/ebooks/53557.

Chapter 7

1. www.archives.gov/publications/prologue/2005/spring/winema.html and www.nps.gov/labe/planyourvisit/upload/MODOC%20WAR.pdf.

2. From "An Indigenous Peoples'History of the United States." http://accuracy.org/americas-longest-war; see also, www.aclu.org/sites/default/files/pdfs/ Safe-free/yoo-army-torture-memo.pdf and www.indianz.com/News/2014/12/17/boyd-cothran-torture-justified-by-treatment-of-Indian-prisoners/.

3. www.haywardareahistory.org/agricultural-history/.

4. www2.census.gov/library/publications/decennial/1960/populations-volume-1/vol-01-06-d.pdf.

5. http://www.yamatobonsai.org/club-sensei.html.

6. www.gsbfbonsai.org/Articles.asp?ID=267.

7. http://bonsailakemerritt.com/garden/list-of-trees/.

8. www.icu.as.jp/en/about.

9. www.kiwiflyer.co.nz/KiwiFlyer-issue-26-Ag-Planes-2.pdf.

10. http://home.iwichita.com/rh1/hold/av/avhist/a8/a8_moth.htm.

11. sarawakiana.blogspot.com/2009/06/history-of-christ-hospital-kepit-1957.html.

12. Hooper, RR, MC. US Hospital Ships: A Proposal for Their Use in Humanitarian Missions. JAMA 1993;270(5):621-623.

13. contributions38761603-Tomoko-Hooper.

Part III
Chapter 10

1. Cartwright LK. Personality Changes in a Sample of Women Physicians. *Journal of Medical Education* 1977;52:467-474; Cartwright LK. Career Satisfaction and Role Harmony in a Sample of Young Women Physicians. *Journal of Vocational Behavior* 1978;12:184-196; Cartwright LK. *Women Physicians at the Peak of Their Career.* Final Report to Robert Wood Johnson Foundation, 1991; Cartwright LK, Wink P. Personality Change in Women Physicians from Medical Student Years to Mid-40s. *Psychology of Women Quarterly.* 1994; 18:291-308.

Chapter 11

1. Biographical information and documentation on Dr. Wanzer kindly supplied by Robert S. Sherins, MD, UCSF, class of 1963, and available in the Archives of the UCSF School of Medicine, http://www.library.ucsf.edu/collections/archives.

2. "pioneer, n. and adj.". *Shorter Oxford English Dictionary.* 2007, Vol. 2, p. 2216. Oxford University Press. The definition of "pioneer" is a military term that identifies a member of an infantry group going with or ahead of army or regiment to dig trenches, repair roads, and clear terrain in readiness for the main body of troops.

3. Oxford English Dictionary dates 'pioneer' from the French *peonaris* in 1517; https://archive.org/stream/accountslordhig00offigoog#page/n243/ mode/2up/search/peonaris.